Grade K

**Scott Foresman**

# Reader's and Writer's Notebook

## Teacher's Manual

 PEARSON  Glenview, Illinois • Boston, Massachusetts • Chandler, Arizona •
Upper Saddle River, New Jersey

ISBN 13: 978-0-328-48474-4
ISBN 10:     0-328-48474-1

8 9 10 V008 18 17 16 15 14 13 12
CC1

# Unit 2: Look at Us!

# Unit 3: Changes All Around Us

# Unit 4: Let's Go Exploring

# Unit 5: Going Places

# Unit 6: Putting It Together

## Listening Rules

1. Face the person who is speaking.

2. Be quiet while someone is speaking.

3. Pay attention to the speaker.

4. Ask questions if you don't understand.

Name _____

1. Speak clearly.

2. Tell only important ideas.

3. Choose your words carefully.

4. Take turns speaking.

5. Speak one at a time.

Name _____

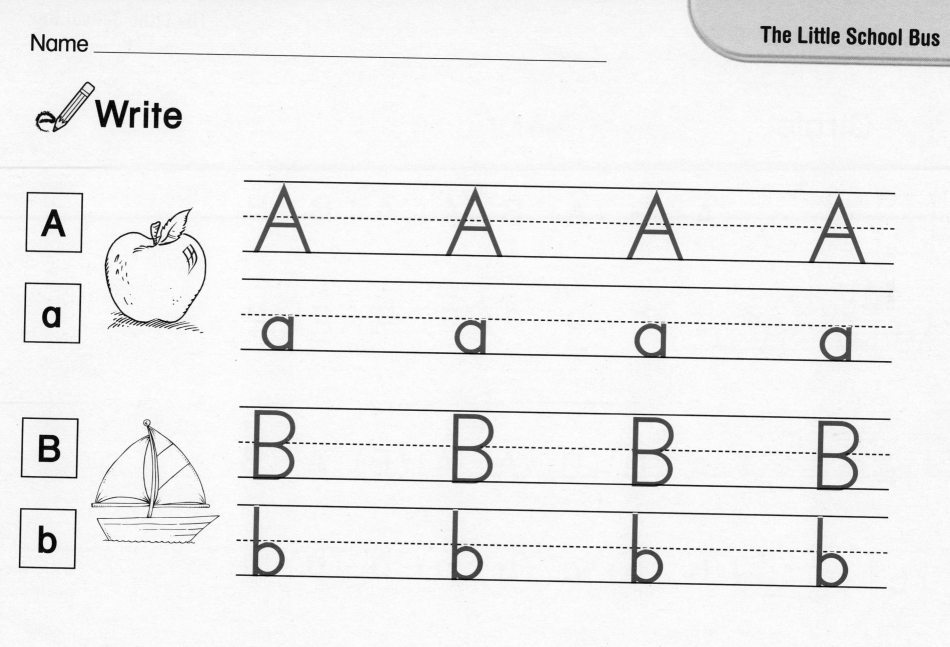

✏️ **Write**

| A |
| a |

| B |
| b |

 **Directions:** Have children write a row of each letter.

 **School + Home** **Home Activity:** Ask your child to show you how to write each letter.

**Handwriting** Letters *A, a* and *B, b*   **3**

Name _____

✏️ **Circle**

A 🍎 (A) A B (A) B (A) (A) B B

a 🐜 (a) b b (a) (a) b (a) b

B 🚣 A (B) (B) A A (B) A (B)

b 🛏️ (b) (b) a (b) a a (b) a

**Directions:** Circle the letters that match the letter in the box.

**Home Activity:** Have your child trace the letters and name the circled letters.

4 **Letter Recognition** *Aa, Bb*

© Pearson Education, Inc., K

# I am bear.

**Decodable Story** *I Am!*
**Letter Recognition** *Aa, Bb, Cc, Dd, Ee*

# I Am!

# I am ant.

I am dog.

I am cat.

Name _____

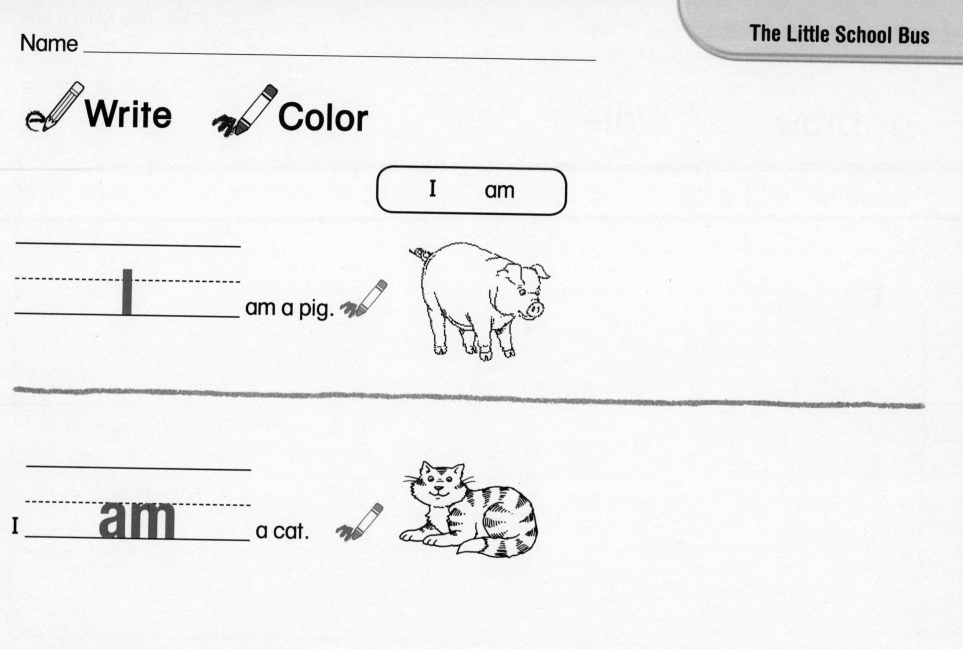

✏️ **Write**    🖍️ **Color**

| I | am |

_____

I _____ am a pig.

I _____ am a cat.

 **Directions:** Read each sentence. Write the missing word to finish the sentence. Color the picture.

 **School + Home** **Home Activity:** Have your child use *I* and *am* in other sentences.

Name _____

 **Draw** **Write**

Answers will vary.

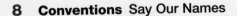 **Directions:** Draw a picture of yourself. Then show your picture and say your name.

 **Home Activity:** Help your child say the names of the people in your family.

Name _____

# ✏ Circle

| C | 🐱 | Ⓒ A Ⓒ B<br>B Ⓒ A Ⓒ |
|---|---|---|

| c | 🚗 | b Ⓒ Ⓒ a<br>Ⓒ a b Ⓒ |
|---|---|---|

| D | 🐶 | C Ⓓ Ⓓ B<br>Ⓓ C Ⓓ C |
|---|---|---|

| d | 🦆 | b Ⓓ a Ⓓ<br>Ⓓ a b Ⓓ |
|---|---|---|

| E | 🥚 | Ⓔ Ⓔ C B<br>B Ⓔ A Ⓔ |
|---|---|---|

| e | 🐘 | Ⓔ c b Ⓔ<br>Ⓔ a c Ⓔ |
|---|---|---|

 **Directions:** Circle the letters that match the letter in the box.

**School + Home** **Home Activity:** Have your child trace the letters in the air and name the circled letters.

Name _____

 **Circle**  **Color**

 **Directions:** Circle an animal that is not in the story. Color the pictures.

**School + Home** **Home Activity:** Ask your child to tell about the characters in the story.

Name _____

✏ Draw 🖍 Color

# If you're happy and you know it,

Answers will vary.

 **Directions:** Draw a picture to show how you would finish the song. Color your picture.

 **Home Activity:** Help your child think of other ways to finish the song and then sing the song together.

Name _____

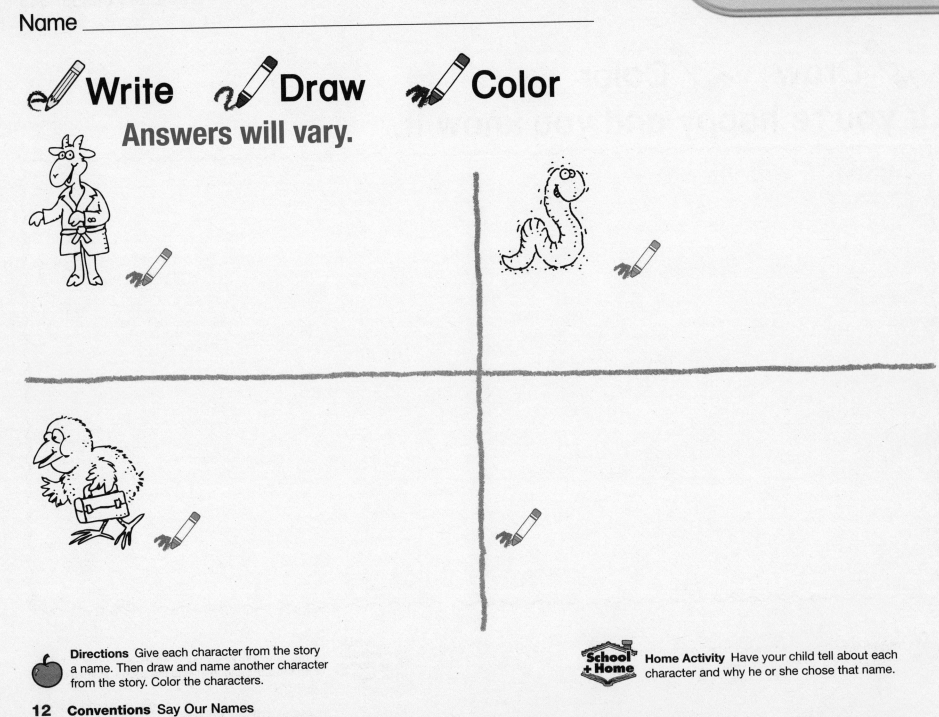

✏️ **Write**  🖍️ **Draw**  🖍️ **Color**

**Answers will vary.**

**Directions** Give each character from the story a name. Then draw and name another character from the story. Color the characters.

**School + Home** **Home Activity** Have your child tell about each character and why he or she chose that name.

Name _____

# ✏️ Write

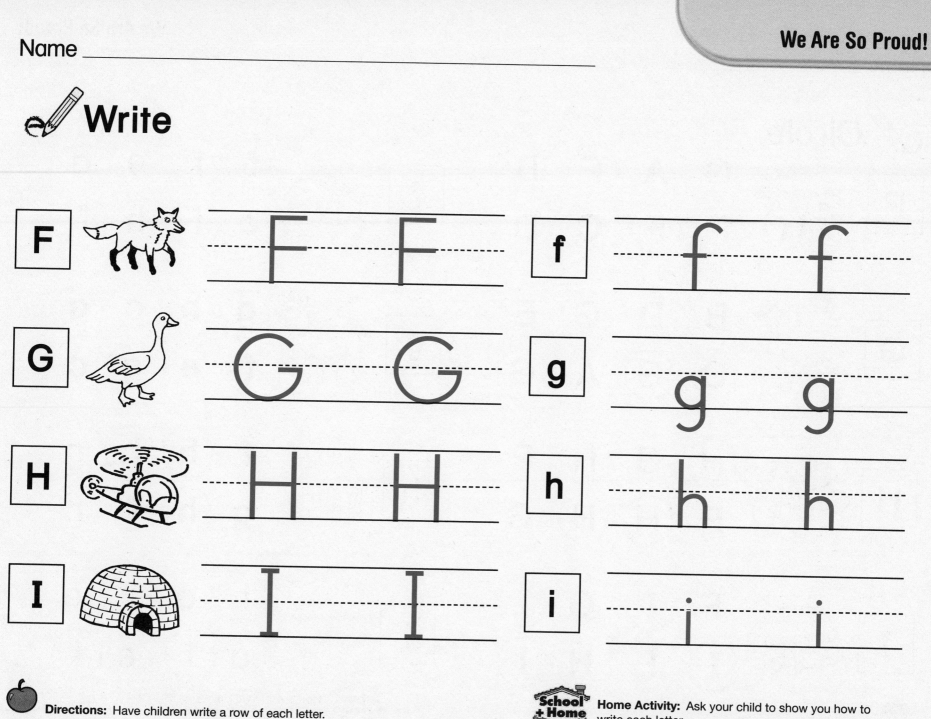

**Directions:** Have children write a row of each letter.

**School + Home**

**Home Activity:** Ask your child to show you how to write each letter.

Name _____

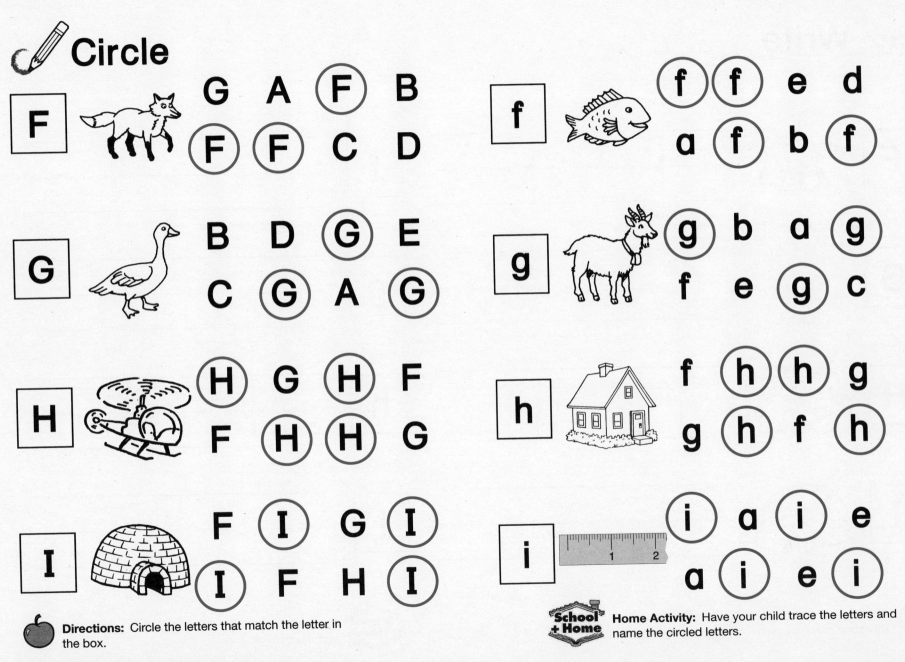

✏️ **Circle**

F | G A (F) B
  | (F) (F) C D

f | f (f) e d
  | a (f) b (f)

G | B D (G) E
  | C (G) A (G)

g | (g) b a (g)
  | f e (g) c

H | (H) G (H) F
  | F (H) (H) G

h | f (h) (h) g
  | g (h) f (h)

I | F (I) G (I)
  | (I) F H (I)

i | i a (i) e
  | a (i) e (i)

🍎 **Directions:** Circle the letters that match the letter in the box.

🏠 **School + Home** **Home Activity:** Have your child trace the letters and name the circled letters.

Am I iguana?

Am I monkey?

Am I kangaroo?

4

**Decodable Story** *Am I?*
**Letter Recognition** *Ff, Gg, Hh, Ii, Jj, Kk, Ll, Mm, Nn*

Name _____

# Am I?

 I am fish.

1

I am goose.

I am horse.

Name _____

✏️ **Write**    🖍️ **Color**

I    am

I ___**am**___ a duck.

___**I**___ am a sheep.

___**I**___ am a frog.

I ___**am**___ a goat.

**Directions:** Read each sentence. Write the missing word to finish the sentence. Color the picture.

**School + Home** **Home Activity:** Have your child use *I* and *am* in other sentences.

© Pearson Education, Inc., K

**High-Frequency Words** **17**

Name _____

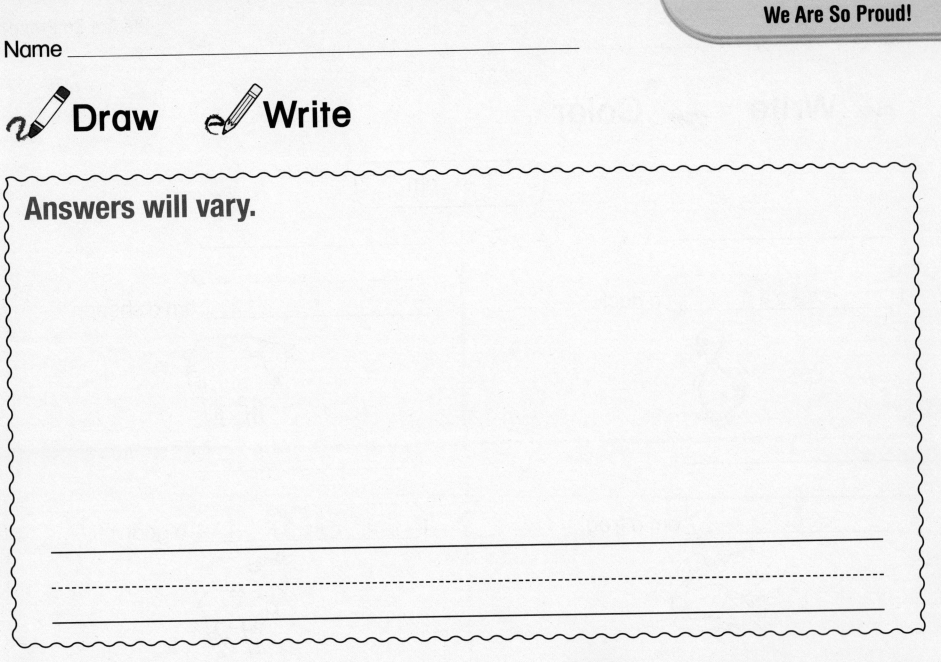

🖍 **Draw**    ✏️ **Write**

Answers will vary.

---

**Directions:** Draw a picture of yourself and write your first name on the line.

**School + Home** **Home Activity:** Help your child write or dictate a list of names of family members and relatives or friends.

Name _____

# ✏️ Circle

| | | | | | | | | |
|---|---|---|---|---|---|---|---|---|
| **Jj** | 🚙 | (J) | H | (j) | g | (j) | (J) | i | G |
| **Kk** | 🦘 | E | (K) | (k) | J | (k) | H | (K) | h |
| **Ll** | 🦁 | (L) | d | (l) | k | (L) | H | K | (l) |
| **Mm** | 🏍️ | H | d | (m) | (M) | h | (M) | W | (m) |
| **Nn** | 🪺 | B | (n) | M | (N) | e | (n) | E | (N) |

🍎 **Directions:** In each row, circle the letters that match the letter or letters in the box.

**School + Home** **Home Activity:** Have your child trace the letters and name the circled letters.

Name _____

# ✏️ Draw

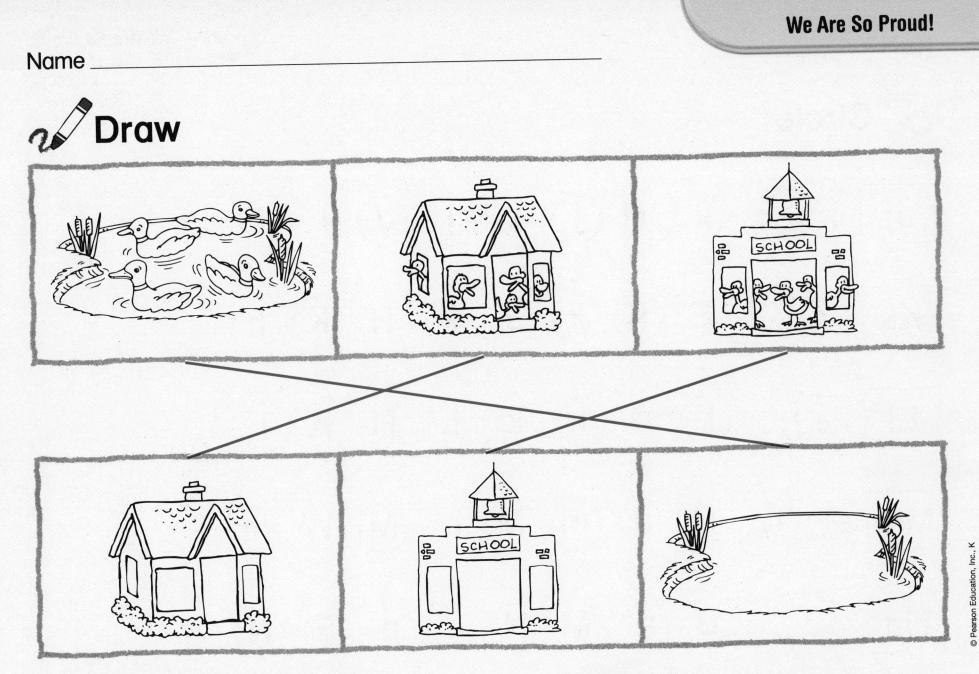

**Directions:** Draw a line from each story in the first row to the picture that shows where the story takes place.

**School + Home**

**Home Activity:** Have your child draw a new setting for a story about the ducks.

Name _____

✏️ **Draw**

Answers will vary.

**Directions** Say your name. Draw a picture that shows something you like to do.

**School + Home** **Home Activity** Ask your child to name some people they know and tell you about each one.

Name _____

**Draw**    **Write**

Answers will vary.

_____

Come to school for _____.

It is on _____

It is at _____ o'clock.

**Directions** Draw a picture for your invitation to a school activity. Write the missing information for the invitation.

**School + Home** **Home Activity** Ask your child to read or tell you the information on the invitation.

Name _____

 Color

 **Directions:** Color the pictures that show characters.

 **Home Activity:** Ask your child to tell you about the teacher in *We Are So Proud!*

**Comprehension** Character **23**

Name _____

✏️ **Write**    🖍️ **Draw**

Answers will vary.

 **Directions** Write your name on the line. Then draw yourself playing your favorite game .

 **Home Activity** Ask your child to tell you about his or her picture.

**24** **Conventions** Write Our Names

Name _____

✏ **Write**

O

o

P

p

🍎 **Directions:** Have children write a row of each letter.

🏫 **School + Home** **Home Activity** Ask your child to show you how to write each letter.

Name _____

 **Circle**

| Oo | Ⓞ N Ⓞ a I e Ⓞ Ⓞ |
| Pp | O Ⓟ b Ⓟ d Ⓟ Ⓟ N |
| Qq | O Ⓠ Ⓠ g H Ⓠ j Ⓠ |
| Rr | P Ⓡ Ⓡ Q Ⓡ n Ⓡ P |
| Ss | Ⓢ L Ⓢ n Ⓢ R o Ⓢ |

 **Directions:** In each row, circle the letters that match the letter or letters in the box.

 **Home Activity:** Have your child trace the letters and name the circled letters.

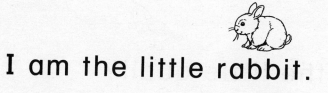

I am the little rabbit.

Am I the little seal?

**Decodable Story** *Little Me!*
**Letter Recognition** *Oo, Pp, Qq, Rr, Ss*

# Little Me!

Am I the little otter?

I am the little otter.

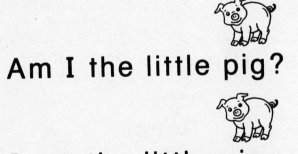 Am I the little pig?

I am the little pig.

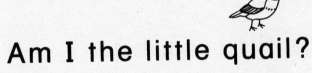 Am I the little quail?

I am the little quail.

Name _____

✏️ Write  🖍️ Color

the    little

The girl is ____ **little** ____.

____ **The** ____ dog is little.

____ **The** ____ cat is little.

The pig is ____ **little** ____.

© Pearson Education, Inc., K

🍎 **Directions:** Read each sentence. Write the missing word to finish the sentence. Color the picture.

**School + Home** **Home Activity:** Have your child use *the* and *little* in other sentences.

Name _____

 **Draw**

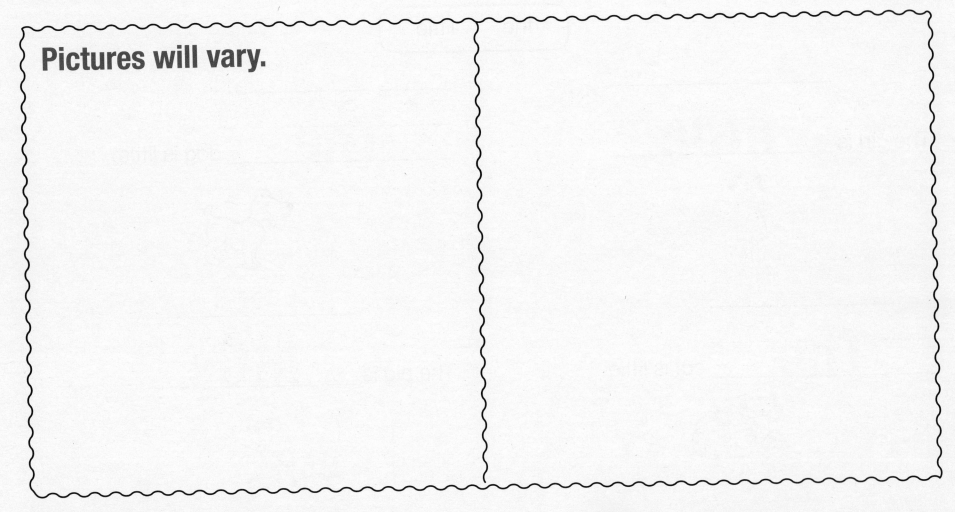

Pictures will vary.

 **Directions:** Draw a picture to show how Plaidypus looks at the beginning of the story and how he looks at the end of the story.

 **Home Activity:** Show pictures to your child and have him or her tell how the people in the pictures look.

Name _____

# ✏ Circle

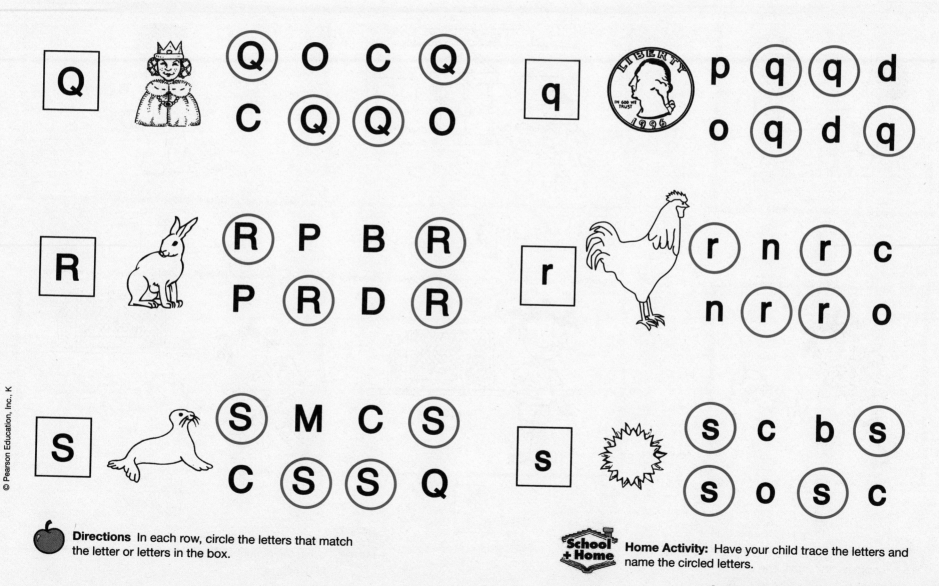

| | | |
|---|---|---|
| Q | 👑 | **Q** O C **Q** / C **Q** **Q** O |
| q | 🪙 | p **p** **q** d / o **q** d **q** |
| R | 🐰 | **R** P B **R** / P **R** D **R** |
| r | 🐓 | **r** n **r** c / n **r** **r** o |
| S | 🦭 | **S** M C **S** / C **S** **S** Q |
| s | ☀ | **s** c b **s** / **s** o **s** c |

🍎 **Directions** In each row, circle the letters that match the letter or letters in the box.

🏠 **School + Home** **Home Activity:** Have your child trace the letters and name the circled letters.

Name _____

# ✏️ Number

3

2

1

1

3

2

**Directions:** Number the pictures to show what happens first, next, and last.

© Pearson Education, Inc., K

**School + Home** **Home Activity:** Have your child make up a story using the pictures to tell what happens first, next, and last.

Name _____

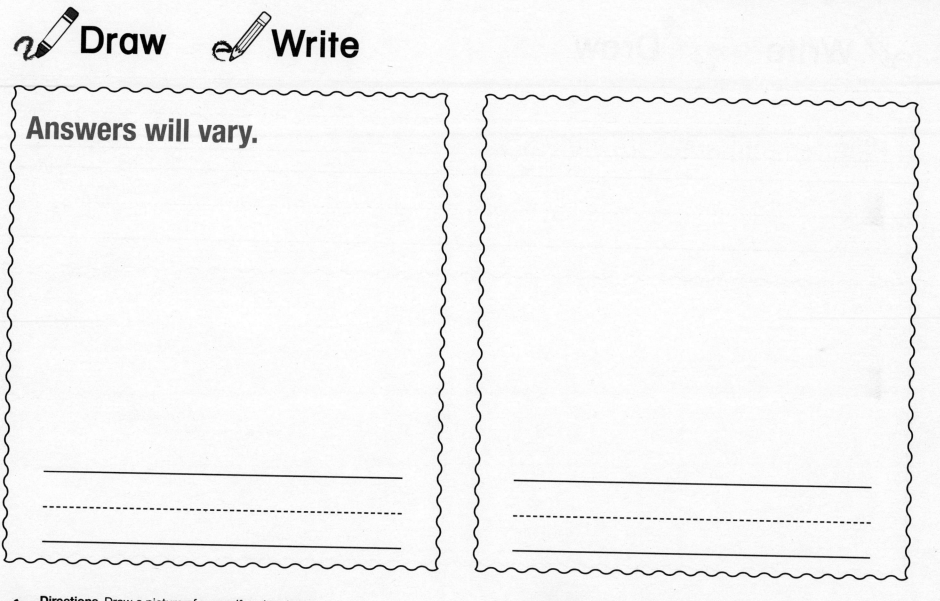

✏️ Draw   ✏️ Write

Answers will vary.

**Directions** Draw a picture of yourself and a picture of someone you know. Write your name and write or dictate the other person's name under the pictures.

**Home Activity** Ask your child to name the people and tell you about each one.

Name _____

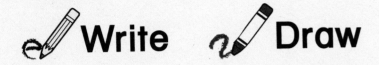 Write  Draw

Pictures and answers will vary.

 **Directions** Copy the lines from the board. Then draw a picture that tells about something you know that goes fast and slow.

 **School + Home** **Home Activity** Have your child read the poem and describe the item that he or she drew that goes fast and slow.

Name _____

# ✏️ Color

🍎 **Directions:** Color the pictures that show settings for stories.

  **Home Activity:** Ask your child to describe what he or she might do in the settings he or she colored.

Name _____

✏️ **Draw**

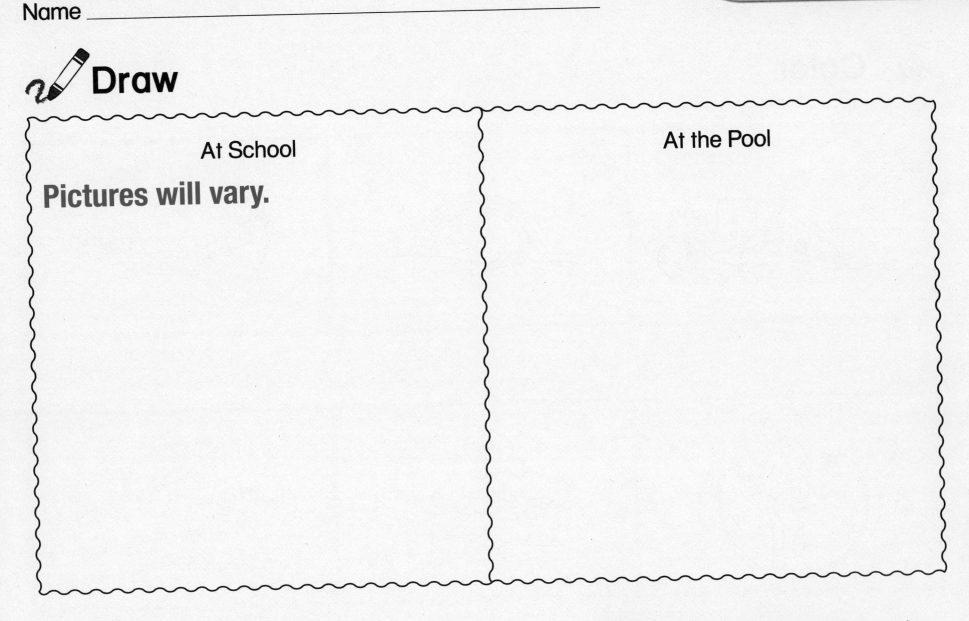

At School

**Pictures will vary.**

At the Pool

**Home Activity** Ask your child to tell about each picture and to describe the way he or she looks at each place.

🍎 **Directions** Draw pictures to show what you look like when you are at school and at the pool.

Name _____

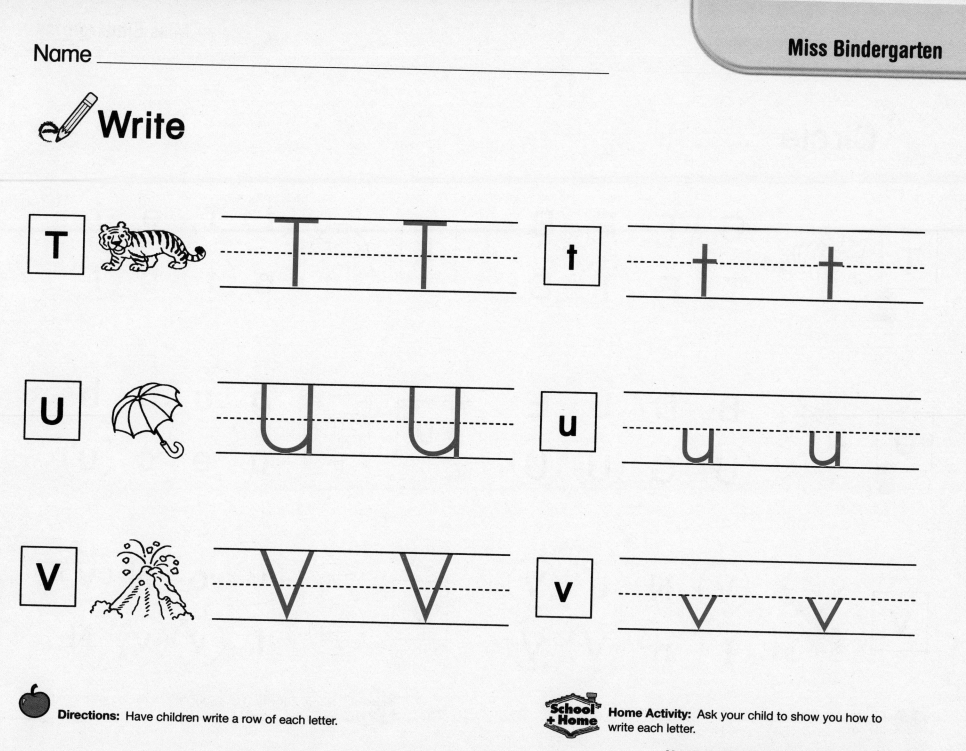

✏ **Write**

T

U

V

t

u

v

**Directions:** Have children write a row of each letter.

**Home Activity:** Ask your child to show you how to write each letter.

Name _____

✏️ **Circle**

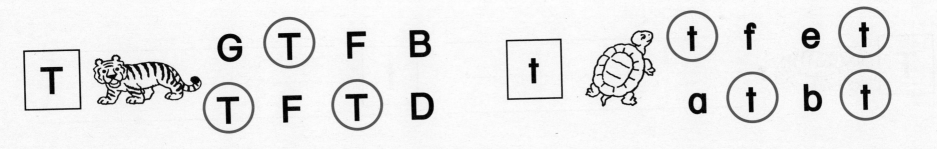

T | 🐅 | G **T** F B
        **T** F **T** D

t | 🐢 | **t** f e **t**
        a **t** b **t**

U | ☂️ | B D **U** E
        **U** G **U** **U**

u | 🪑 | g **u** a b
        **u** e c **u**

V | 🎻 | **V** N u **V**
        I n **V** **V**

v | 🏺 | **v** o N **V**
        f **v** **v** N

 **Directions:** Circle the letters that match the letter in the box.

🏠 **School + Home** **Home Activity:** Have your child trace the letters and name the circled letters.

Am I the little zebra?

© Pearson Education, Inc., K

Name _____

# Am I Little?

Am I the little turtle?

Am I the little van?

Am I the little

watermelon?

Name _____

Write    Color

| the    little |
|---------------|

_____
**The** dog can sleep.

_____
I have a **little** dog.

_____
Did you feed **the** dog?

_____
The **little** dog sleeps.

**Directions:** Read each sentence. Write the missing word to finish the sentence. Color the picture.

**School + Home** **Home Activity:** Have your child use *the* and *little* in other sentences.

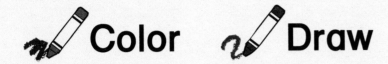 **Color** **Draw**

Answers will vary.

**Directions:** Color the What We Can Do pictures in the top row. In the bottom row, draw pictures of other What We Can Do activities . Then tell about the things we can do.

 **Home Activity:** Ask your child to tell you about something he or she likes to do.

Name _____

✏️ **Circle**

| | | | | | | | | | |
|---|---|---|---|---|---|---|---|---|---|
| **Ww** | 🏉 | (W) | T | F | (w) | f | e | (w) | (W) |

| | | | | | | | | | |
|---|---|---|---|---|---|---|---|---|---|
| **Xx** | 🖐️ | B | (X) | D | (X) | (x) | u | d | (x) |

| | | | | | | | | | |
|---|---|---|---|---|---|---|---|---|---|
| **Yy** | 🧶 | (Y) | X | (y) | v | (Y) | W | (y) | u |

| | | | | | | | | | |
|---|---|---|---|---|---|---|---|---|---|
| **Zz** | 🦓 | x | (z) | Y | (Z) | X | (z) | V | (Z) |

🍎 **Directions:** Circle the letters that match the letter in the box.

 **Home Activity:** Have your child trace and name the circled letters.

Name _____

 Circle  Color

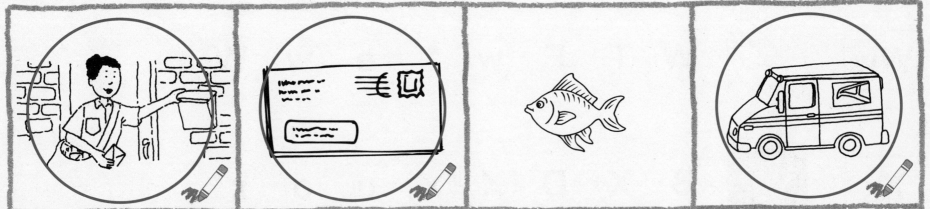

**Directions:** Circle items in each row that belong together. Color those pictures.

**School + Home** **Home Activity:** Have your child draw three items that belong in a kitchen.

**44** **Comprehension** Classify and Categorize

Name _____

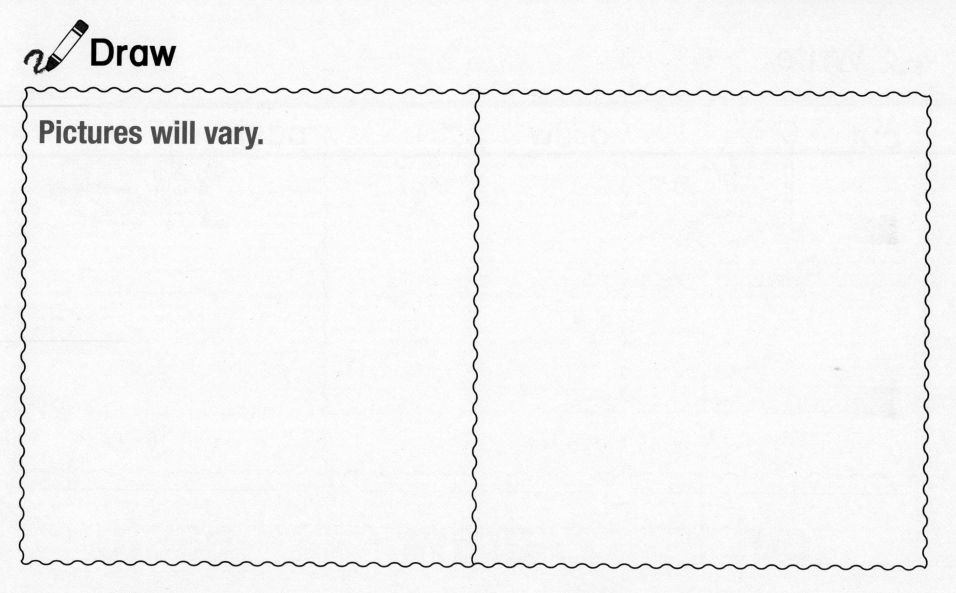

# Draw

Pictures will vary.

 **Directions** Draw pictures to show two characters on the field trip from the story.

 **Home Activity** Ask your child to name the characters and tell you about each one.

Name _____

✏️ **Write**

cut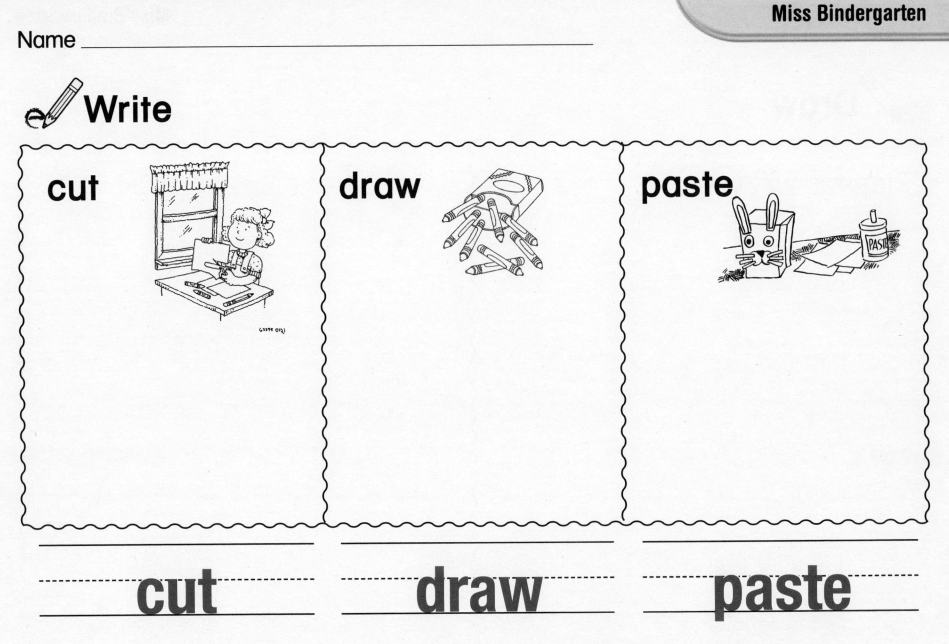

draw

paste

_____

- - - - - **cut** _____

- - - - - **draw** _____

- - - - - **paste** _____

🍎 **Directions** These are the words we use to give instructions. Write the word that goes with each picture to give instructions for making a rabbit.

 **School + Home** **Home Activity** Have your child tell how to make the rabbit.

Name _____

## ✏️ **Draw**

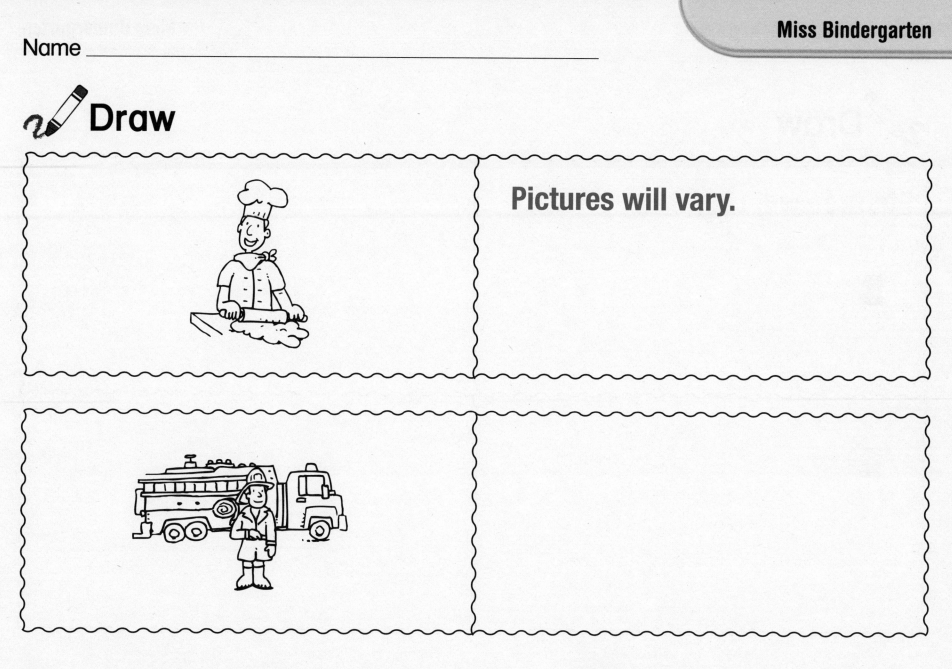

**Pictures will vary.**

 **Directions** Look at each story character. Draw a picture to show the story setting for that character.

 **School + Home** **Home Activity** Ask your child to name the characters and tell you about each one.

Name _____

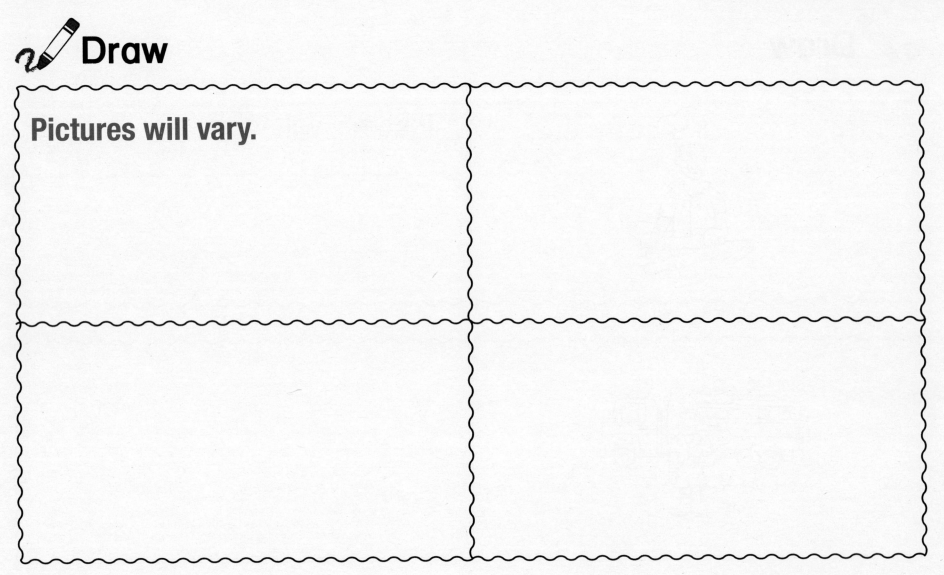

## Draw

**Pictures will vary.**

**Directions** Draw pictures to show things you like to do. Then choose your favorite and tell about the favorite thing you like to do.

 **Home Activity** Ask your child to tell about other things he or she likes to do.

Name _____

 **Write**

M   M   M   M   M   M

m   m   m   m   m   m

**Mom**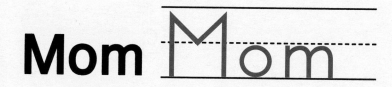

**am** am

 **Directions:** Have children write a row of each letter and then write the words.

 **Home Activity:** Ask your child to show you how to write each letter.

Name _____

✏️ **Write**   🖍️ **Color**

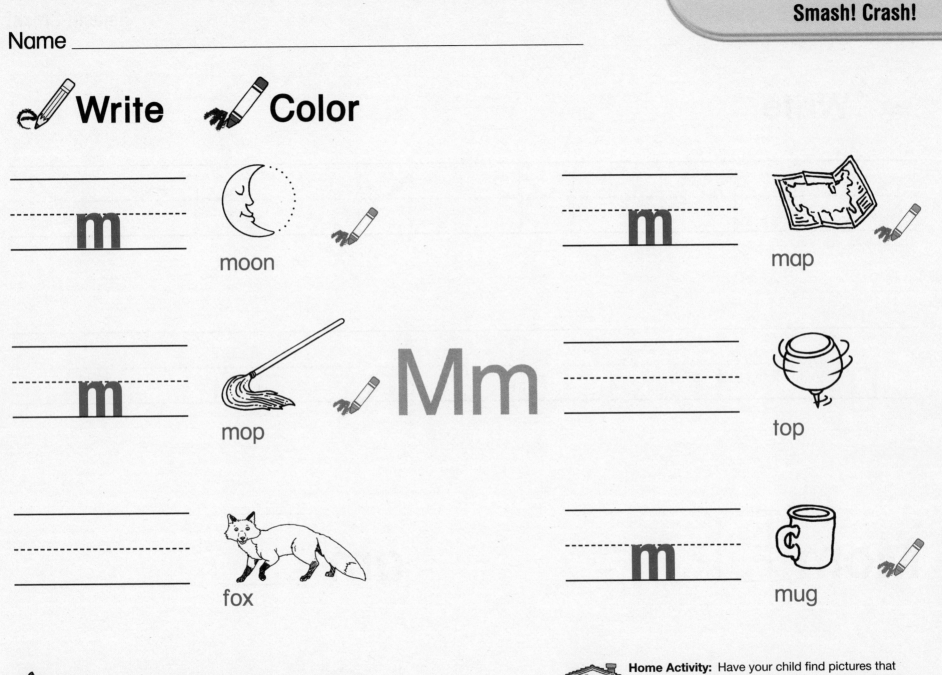

m — moon

m — mop

_____ — fox

Mm

m — map

_____ — top

m — mug

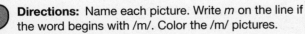**Directions:** Name each picture. Write *m* on the line if the word begins with /m/. Color the /m/ pictures.

**School + Home**  **Home Activity:** Have your child find pictures that begin with /m/ and paste the pictures on paper to make an /m/ book.

 I walk to a little school.

**Decodable Story** *Little Mouse*
**Target Skill** /m/ Spelled *Mm*

Name _____

# Little Mouse

 I am a little mouse.

I walk to a little school.

I am a little moose.

Name _____

✏️ **Write**   🖍️ **Color**

| to   a |

_____
Tim has ____**a**____ map.

_____
Tim went ____**to**____ school.

_____
Pam went ____**to**____ school.

_____
Pam has ____**a**____ top.

**Directions:** Read each sentence. Write the missing word to finish the sentence. Color the picture.

**School + Home**   **Home Activity:** Have your child use the high-frequency words in other sentences.

Name _____

 # Read It!

I see a boy.

# Say It!

Say a sentence about something a dog does.

 # Write It!

_____

I see a _____**cat**_____. (cat)

**Directions:** Have children read the sentence about the boy with you. Ask them to give a sentence about a dog. Then have children write the word for an animal to complete the sentence.

 **Home Activity:** Ask your child to name other people and animals.

Name _____

✏️ Write    🖍️ Color

jam

cat

dog

Mm

gum

drum

yam

🍎 **Directions:** Name each picture. Write *m* on the line if the word ends with /m/. Color the /m/ pictures.

 **Home Activity:** Have your child find an object at home that ends with /m/.

Name _____

# Color

color boy

color animal

color girl

color woman

**Directions:** Color the character in each box. Then tell about the character in each box.

**School + Home**

**Home Activity:** Ask your child to tell you about the characters in one of his or her favorite stories.

Name _____

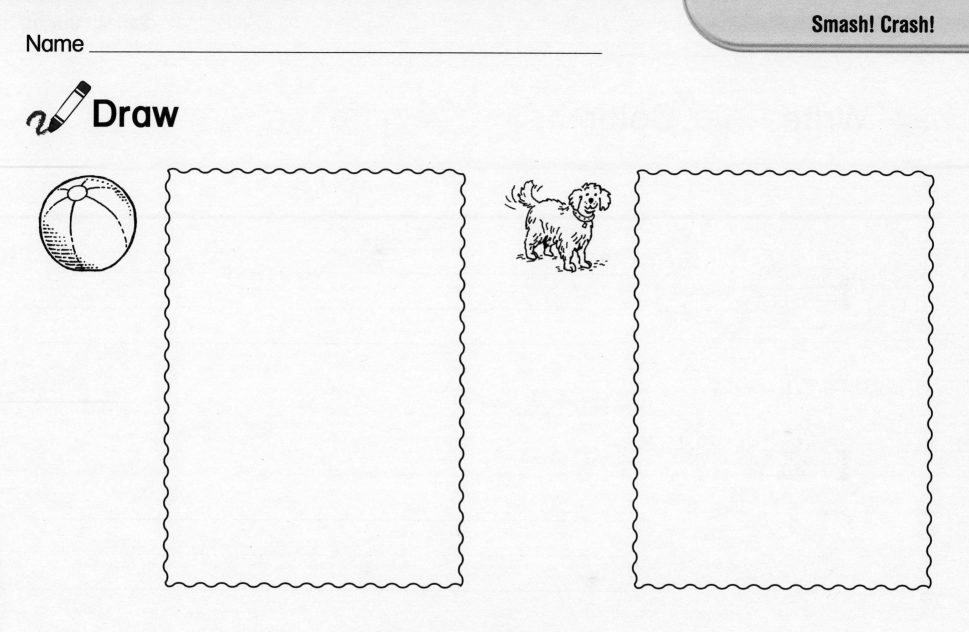

✏️ **Draw**

**Pictures will vary.**

🍎 **Directions** Draw pictures to show what you would do with the ball and the dog. Then tell what you are doing in each picture.

 **Home Activity** Have your child tell what he or she likes to do.

Name _____

 **Write**   **Color**

**Answers will vary.**

 **Directions** Write or dictate a caption for each picture. Color the pictures.

 **Home Activity** Help your child create other captions for each picture.

**58** **Writing** Captions

Name _____

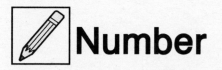**Number**

3     1     2

2     3     1

**Directions:** Number the pictures to show what happens first, next, and last.

**School + Home**

**Home Activity:** Ask your child to tell you how to do a task. Remind him or her to give the steps in the correct order.

Name _____

 **Read It!**

I see a cook.

**Say It!**

Say a sentence about
what a horse looks like.

 **Write It!**

_____

I see a _____ **bird** _____ . (bird)

**Directions** Have children read the sentence about
the cook with you. Ask them to give a sentence about
a horse. Then have children write the word for an
animal to complete the sentence.

 **Home Activity** Point to each item. Have your child
name the item and tell whether it is a person or an
animal.

**60** **Conventions** Nouns for People and Animals

Name _____

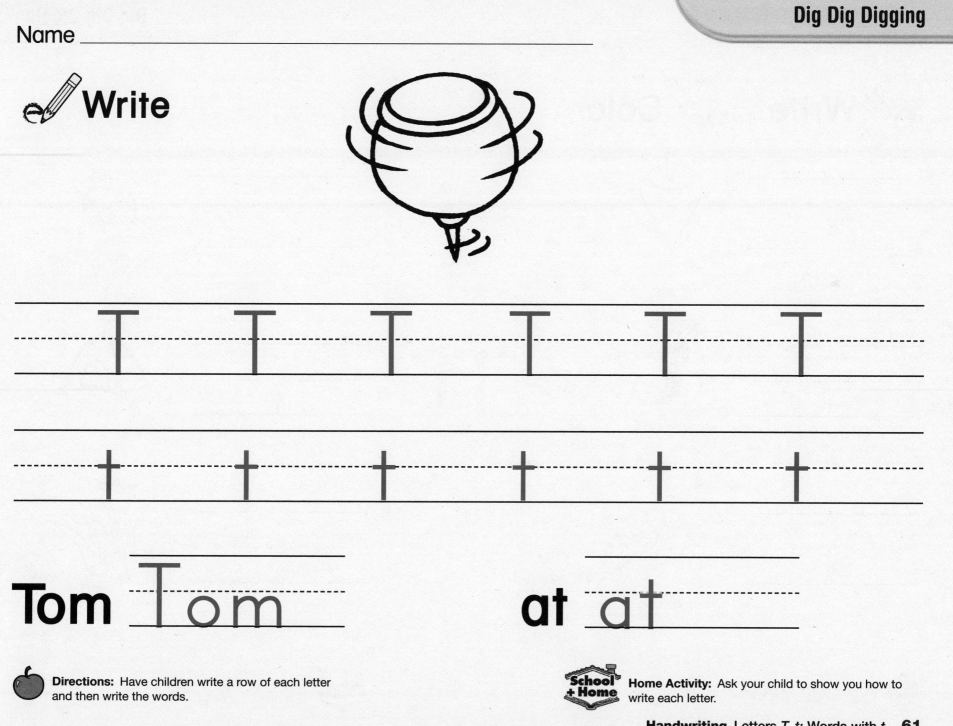

✏️ **Write**

T T T T T T

t t t t t t

**Tom** Tom

**at** at

**Directions:** Have children write a row of each letter and then write the words.

**Home Activity:** Ask your child to show you how to write each letter.

**Handwriting** Letters *T, t:* Words with *t* **61**

Name _____

✏ **Write**   🖍 **Color**

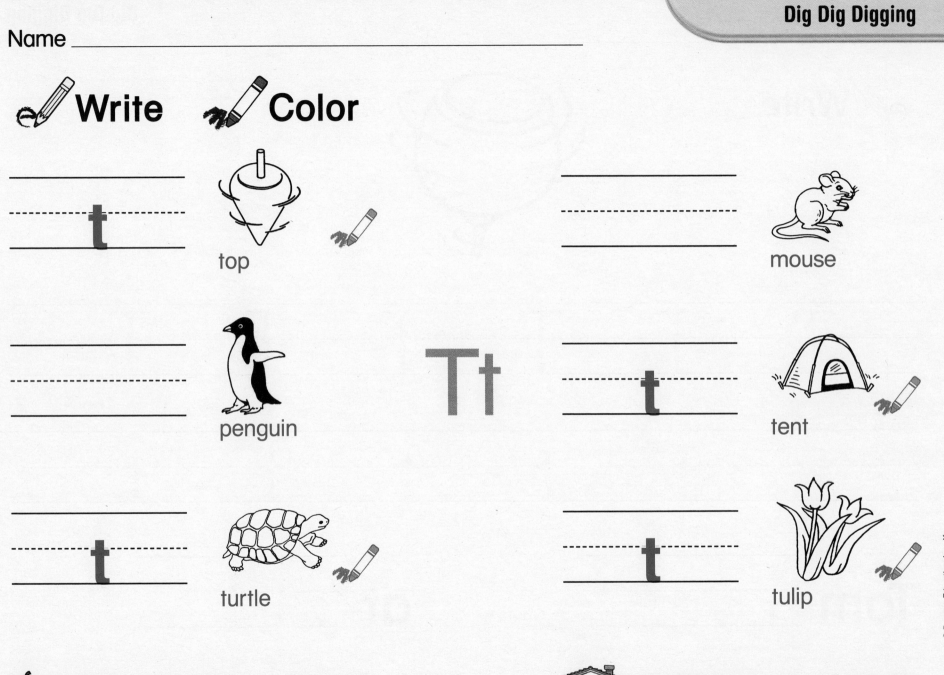

top

penguin

turtle

Tt

mouse

tent

tulip

**Directions:** Name each picture. Write *t* on the line if the word begins with /t/. Color the /t/ pictures.

**Home Activity:** Have your child trace the target letter and name the pictures that begin with *Tt*.

I walk to a table.

---

Name _____

# Tam!

I am Tam.

I am a turtle.

 **I walk to a tent.**

2

 **I walk to a turkey.**

3

Name _____

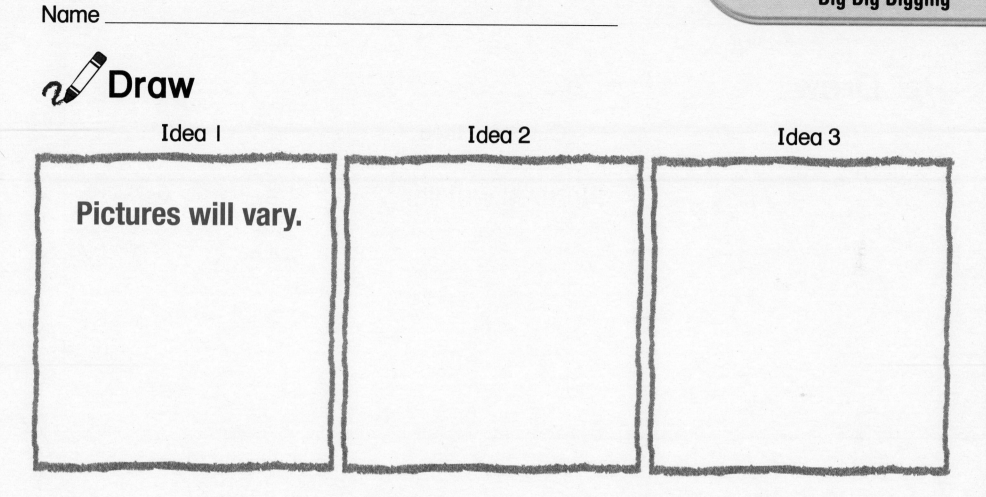

## Draw

Idea 1

Idea 2

Idea 3

**Pictures will vary.**

 **Directions** Have children draw pictures of activities they do together as a class.

 **Home Activity** Ask your child to tell you about the activities in the pictures.

**Writing Process** Planning  **65**

Name _____

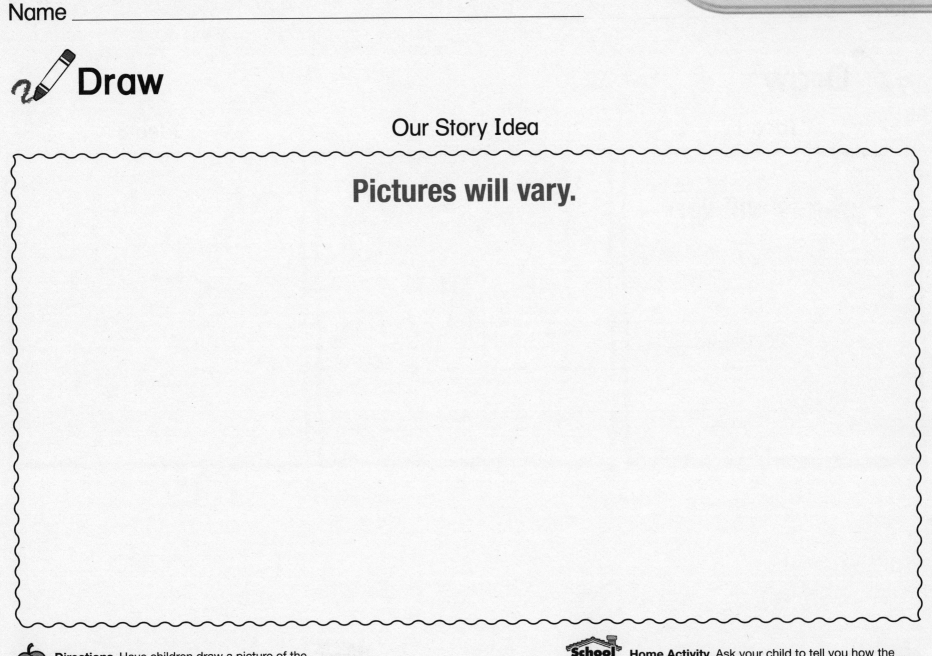

# ✏️ Draw

## Our Story Idea

**Pictures will vary.**

🍎 **Directions** Have children draw a picture of the class's story idea.

 **Home Activity** Ask your child to tell you how the picture shows the class's story idea.

Name _____

✏️ Write ✏️ Color

| to    a    little    am |

_____

I am _____ **a** _____ cat.

I _____ **am** _____ a little cat.

_____

I go _____ **to** _____ school.

The house is _____ **little** _____.

🍎 **Directions:** Read each sentence. Write the missing word to finish the sentence. Color the picture.

**School + Home** **Home Activity:** Have your child use the high-frequency words in other sentences.

Name _____

 **Read It!**

I see a book.

**Say It!**

Say a sentence that tells about your favorite book.

 **Write It!**

_____

I see a _____ **park** _____ . (park)

**Directions** Have children read the sentence about the book with you. Ask them to give a sentence about the books in the picture. Then have children write the noun for a place to complete the sentence .

 **School + Home** **Home Activity** Ask your child to name other items that are places and things.

Name _____

 **Draw**

| Beginning | Middle | End |
|---|---|---|
| Pictures will vary. | | |

**Directions** Have children draw pictures of the events for the beginning, middle, and end of the class story.

 **School + Home** **Home Activity** Have your child tell you the sequence of events in the class story.

Name _____

## Write    **Answers will vary.**

**Beginning**

_____
- - - - - - - - - - - - - - - - - - - - - - - - - -
_____

**Middle**

_____
- - - - - - - - - - - - - - - - - - - - - - - - - -
_____

**End**

_____
- - - - - - - - - - - - - - - - - - - - - - - - - -
_____

**Directions** Have children write or dictate words or sentences that tell the beginning, middle, and end of the class story.

**School + Home** **Home Activity** Ask your child to read the words or sentences to you.

Name _____

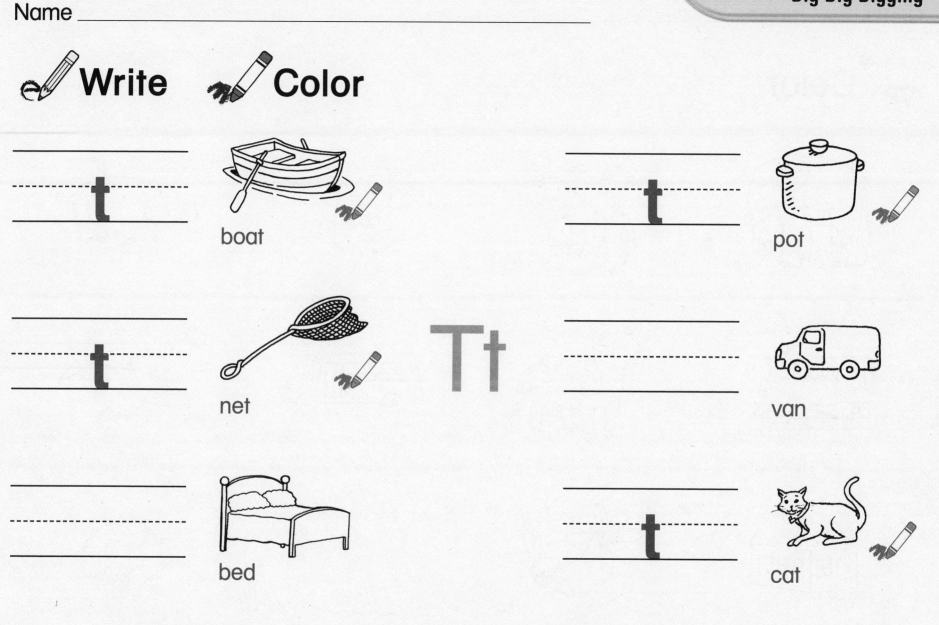

✏️ **Write**     🖍️ **Color**

t     boat

t     pot

t     net

**Tt**

van

bed

t     cat

 **Directions:** Name each picture. Write *t* on the line if the word ends with /t/. Color the /t/ pictures.

 **Home Activity:** Have your child draw a picture of something that ends with /t/ and write the word.

Name _____

✏️ **Color**

---

_(Row 1: elephant, tiger, leaf, hippo)_

---

_(Row 2: train, cow, bus, airplane)_

---

_(Row 3: house, flower, tree, bush)_

🍎 **Directions:** Color the pictures in each row that belong to the same group.

**School + Home** **Home Activity:** Ask your child to sort toys into groups by color, size, or shape.

**72** **Comprehension** Classify and Categorize

Name _____

 **Read It!**

I see a girl.

**Say It!**

Say a sentence about the teacher.

 **Write It!**

_____

I see a _____ **hen** _____. (hen)

 **Directions** Have children read the sentence about the girl with you. Ask them to give a sentence about the teacher. Then have children write the word that names the animal to complete the sentence.

 **School + Home** **Home Activity** Ask your child to name other naming words (nouns) for people and animals.

**Conventions** Nouns for People and Animals   **73**

Name _____

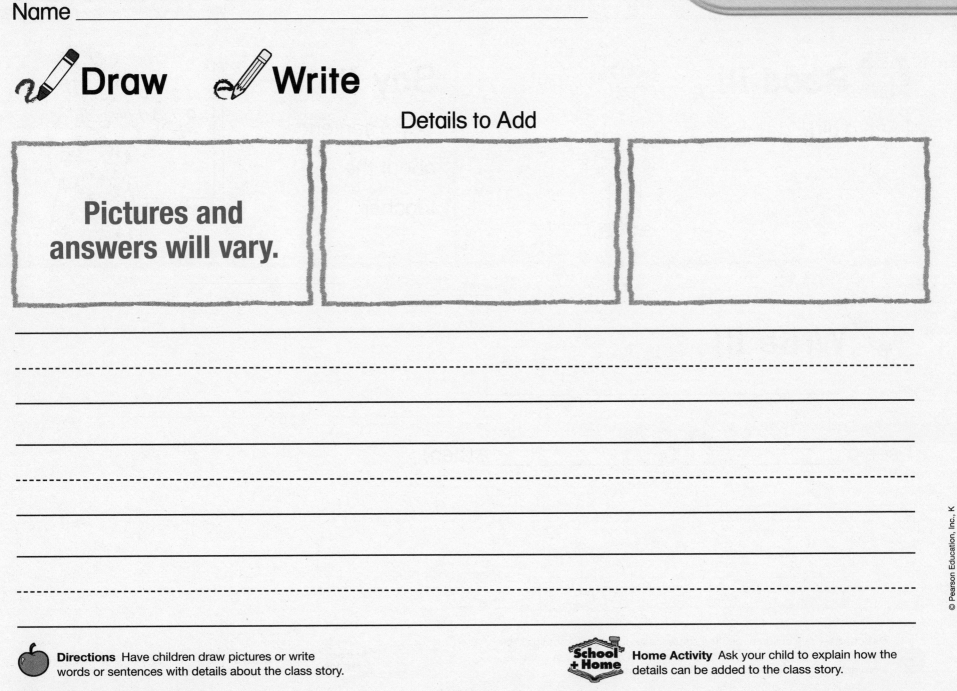

✏️ Draw   ✏️ Write

Details to Add

Pictures and answers will vary.

**Directions** Have children draw pictures or write words or sentences with details about the class story.

**School + Home** **Home Activity** Ask your child to explain how the details can be added to the class story.

Name _____

✏️ Color

**Directions:** Look at the picture at the top of the page. Color the pictures in the boxes that are part of the setting.

 **Home Activity:** Have your child make up a story to go with the top picture.

Name _____

 **Read It!**

I see a house.

**Say It!**

Say a sentence that tells about a tree.

 **Write It!**

_____

I see a _____**bus**_____. (bus)

**Directions** Have children read the sentence about the house with you. Ask them to give a sentence about the tree in the picture. Then have children write the noun for a thing to complete the sentence.

 **Home Activity** Ask your child to name the items and then name other items that are places or things.

Name _____

✏ Circle    ✏ Write

I. We (like) (m u s i c).

_____

- - - - - - - - - - - - - - - - - - - - - - - - - - - - - - - - - -

_____

2. (Thisis) a (new    song).

- - - - - - - - - - - - - - - - - - - - - - - - - - - - - - - - - -

_____

3. (She    plays) (forus).

_____

- - - - - - - - - - - - - - - - - - - - - - - - - - - - - - - - - -

_____

🍎 **Directions** Have children circle the mistakes and rewrite the words or sentences correctly on the lines.

 **Home Activity** Ask your child to explain why correct spacing between letters and words is important.

© Pearson Education, Inc., K

Name _____

# Write

**Directions** Have children copy sentences from the class story using correct spacing between letters and words.

**Home Activity** Help your child edit the sentences by checking for correct letter and word spacing.

Name _____

**✏ Draw**    **✏ Write**

Answers will vary.

_____

- - - - - - - - - - - - - - - - - - - - - - - - - - - - - - - - - - - - - - - - -

Title: _____

_____

- - - - - - - - - - - - - - - - - - - - - - - - - - - - - - - - - - - - - - - - -

Author: _____

**Directions** Have children draw a picture for a cover of their story. Help them write the story's title and their name.

**Home Activity** Have your child explain how the picture and title go with the story.

Name _____

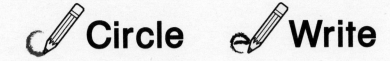 Circle  Write

I shared my story with **Answers will vary.** .

Here's what he / she thought about my story.

**Answers will vary.**

© Pearson Education, Inc., K

**Directions** Have children circle the picture that shows with whom they shared their story. Then have children ask the peer or adult reviewer to fill in the blanks and to discuss the story with him or her.

 **Home Activity** Ask your child to read or tell the class story to you.

Name _____

**Write**

A A A A A A A

a a a a a a a

am  am

at  at

**Directions:** Have children write a row of each letter and then write the words.

**School + Home**

**Home Activity:** Ask your child to show you how to write each letter.

**Handwriting** Letters A, a: Words with a  **81**

Name _____

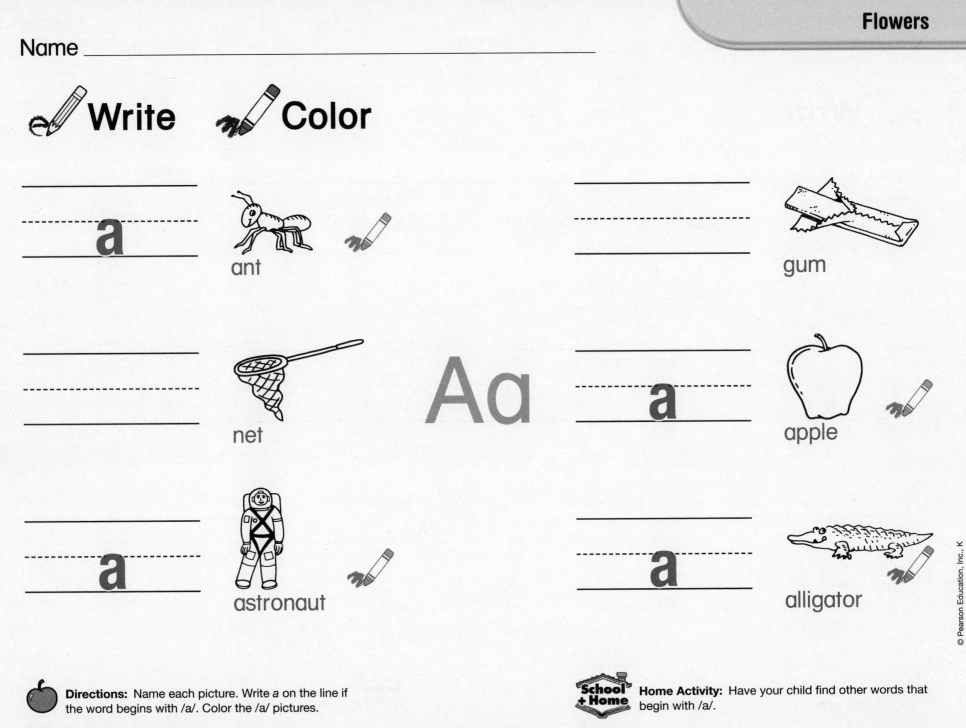

Write　　Color

a　　ant

net

a　　astronaut

Aa

gum

a　　apple

a　　alligator

**Directions:** Name each picture. Write *a* on the line if the word begins with /a/. Color the /a/ pictures.

**School + Home** **Home Activity:** Have your child find other words that begin with /a/.

82　**Phonics** /a/ Spelled *Aa*

I have gum.

© Pearson Education, Inc., K

# I Have!

I have a cat.

The cat is little.

I have a rat.

The rat is little.

2

I have a ham.

The ham is little.

3

Name _____

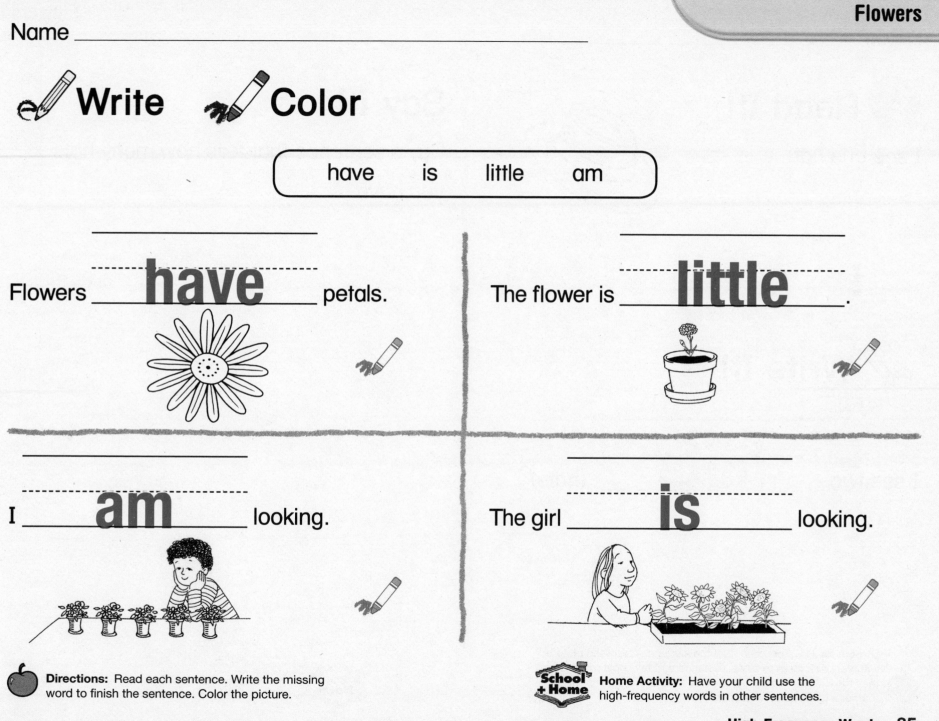

✏️ Write 🖍️ Color

have        is        little        am

Flowers ____**have**____ petals.

The flower is ____**little**____.

I ____**am**____ looking.

The girl ____**is**____ looking.

**Directions:** Read each sentence. Write the missing word to finish the sentence. Color the picture.

**School + Home**

**Home Activity:** Have your child use the high-frequency words in other sentences.

Name _____

 **Read It!**

I see one hat.

**Say It!**

Say a sentence that tells how many hats you have.

 **Write It!**

_____

I see two ___**hats**___. (hats)

**Directions** Have children read the sentence about the picture with you. Ask them to say a sentence that tells how many hats they have. Then have children write a word that means more than one to complete the sentence.

 **School + Home** **Home Activity** Ask your child to tell which word tells one and which tells more than one.

Name _____

**Write**    **Color**

man

a    ant

Aa

cat

a    add    1 + 1 = 2

rat

a    apple

**Directions:** Name each picture. Write *a* on the line if the word begins with /a/. Color the pictures with middle /a/.

**Home Activity:** Have your child find an object at home that begins with *a*, draw a picture of it, and write the word.

**School + Home**

**Phonics** /a/ Spelled *Aa*    **87**

Name _____

 Draw ✏️ Color

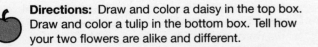 **Directions:** Draw and color a daisy in the top box. Draw and color a tulip in the bottom box. Tell how your two flowers are alike and different.

 **Home Activity:** Have your child explain the similarities and differences between a daisy and a tulip.

**88** **Comprehension** Compare and Contrast

Name _____

###  Read It!

I see a school.

## Say It!

Say a sentence that tells about a place you know.

###  Write It!

_____

I like to play _____**ball**_____. (ball)

**Directions:** Have children read the sentence with a noun that names a place. Ask them to say a sentence about a place they know. Then have children write a word to complete the sentence with a noun that names a thing.

 **School + Home**

**Home Activity:** Have your child tell about places in your neighborhood. Then ask your child to name things found at home.

Name _____

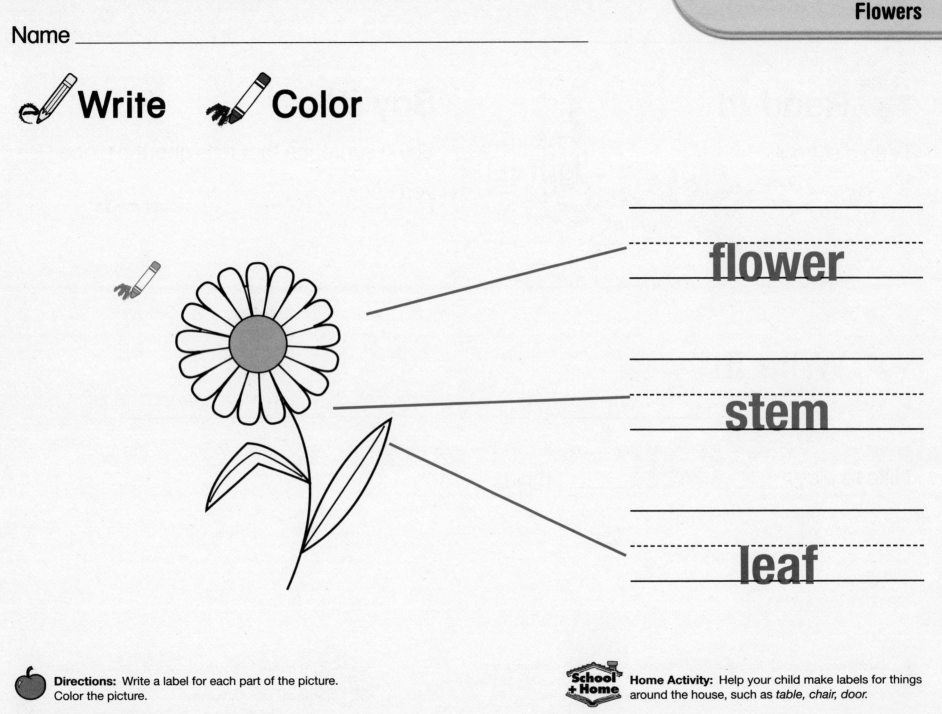

✏️ **Write**   🖍️ **Color**

flower

stem

leaf

**Directions:** Write a label for each part of the picture.
Color the picture.

© Pearson Education, Inc., K

**School + Home** **Home Activity:** Help your child make labels for things around the house, such as *table, chair, door*.

Name _____

 # Color

**Directions:** Color the items in each row that belong together.

**Home Activity:** Name sets of three things and have your child tell you which two belong together and tell why: *knife, fork, book. Knife* and *fork* are silverware.

**Comprehension** Classify and Categorize    **91**

Name _____

 **Read It!**

I see three cats.

**Say It!**

Say a sentence that tells about things you have.

**Write It!**

_____

I have two ____**bats**____. (bats)

**Directions:** Have children read the sentence about the picture with you. Ask them to tell a sentence about things they have. Then have children write the noun for more than one to complete the sentence.

 **Home Activity:** Point to an item (or several items) and have your child name the item.

**92** **Conventions** Nouns for More Than One

Name _____

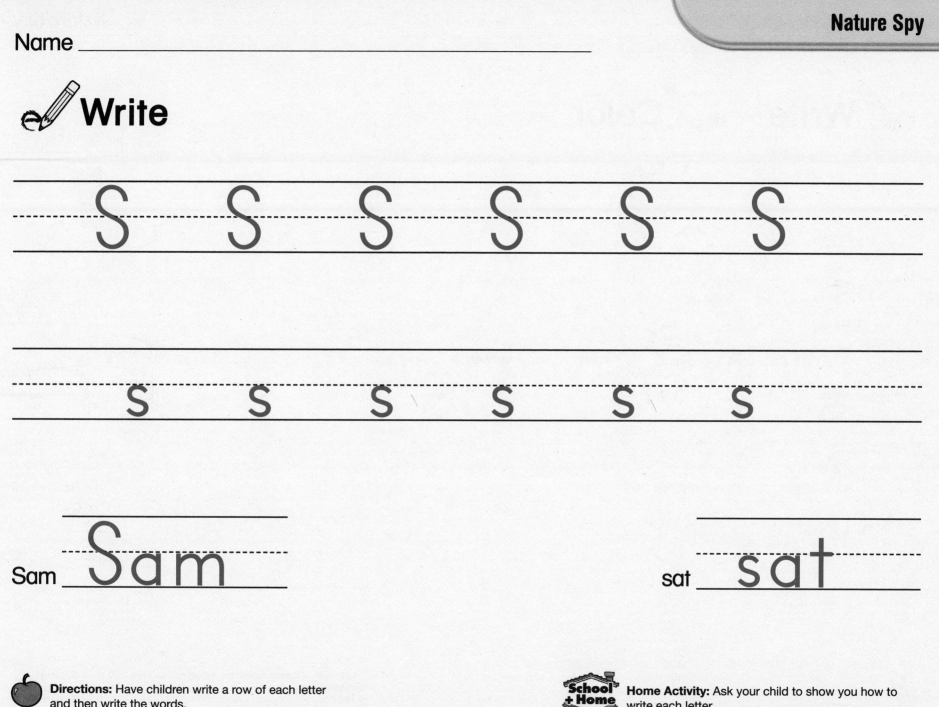

✏️ **Write**

S     S     S     S     S     S

s     s     s     s     s     s

Sam   Sam

sat   sat

 **Directions:** Have children write a row of each letter and then write the words.

**School + Home** **Home Activity:** Ask your child to show you how to write each letter.

Name _____

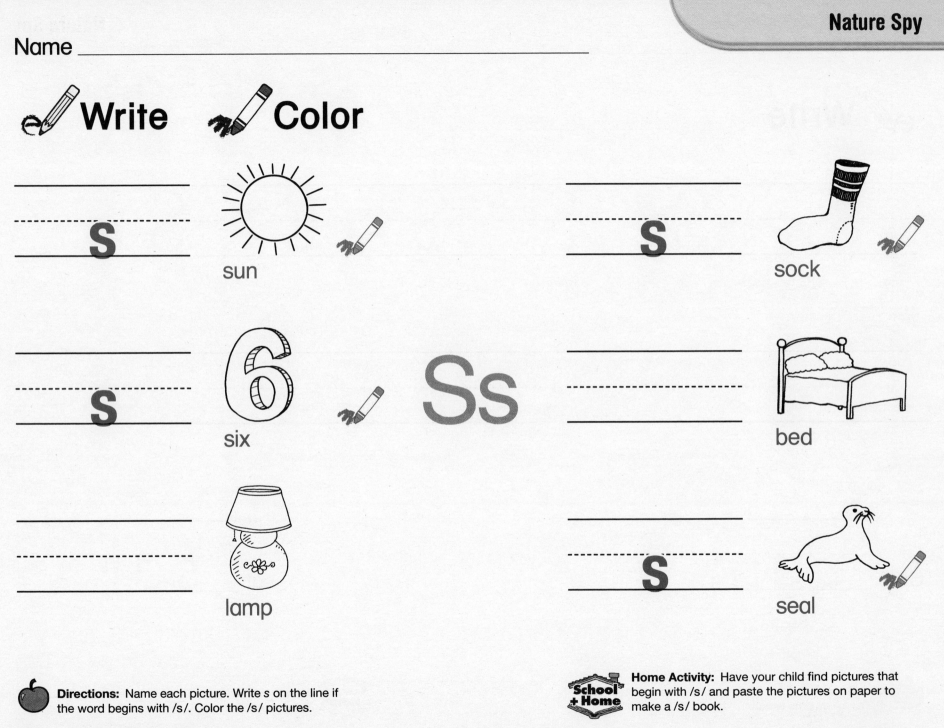

✏️ **Write**  🖍️ **Color**

s — sun

s — six

___ — lamp

**Ss**

s — sock

___ — bed

s — seal

🍎 **Directions:** Name each picture. Write *s* on the line if the word begins with /s/. Color the /s/ pictures.

**Home Activity:** Have your child find pictures that begin with /s/ and paste the pictures on paper to make a /s/ book.

I have the sock.

4

# Sock Sack

I have a sack.

1

The sock sack is little.

The sock is little.

Name _____

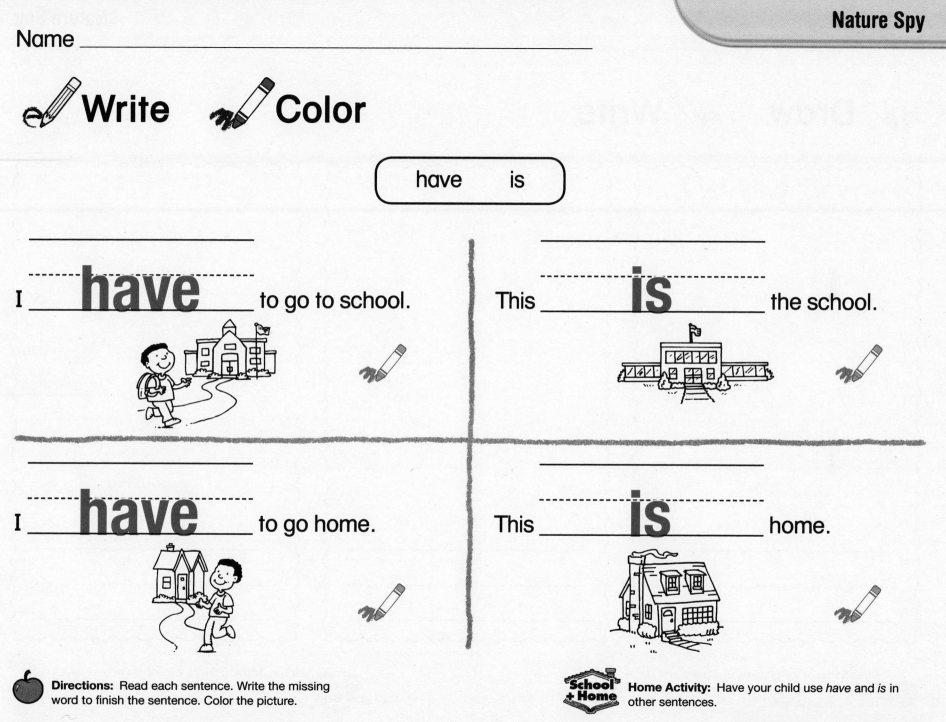

✏️ **Write**    🖍️ **Color**

have    is

I ___**have**___ to go to school.

This ___**is**___ the school.

I ___**have**___ to go home.

This ___**is**___ home.

🍎 **Directions:** Read each sentence. Write the missing word to finish the sentence. Color the picture.

**School + Home** **Home Activity:** Have your child use *have* and *is* in other sentences.

Name _____

✏️ **Draw**   ✏️ **Write**

Answers will vary.

**Directions:** Draw pictures of a pet you know, a friend, and a family member. Use upper-case letters to write their names.

**Home Activity:** Write the names of everyone in your family. Talk with your child about how people's first and last names use uppercase letters.

School + Home

Name _____

✏️ **Write**    🖍️ **Color**

_____
- - - - - - - - - - - -
_____
soap

_____
- - - - - - - - - - - -
_____
seal

**s** _____
gas

**Ss**

_____
- - - - - - - - - - - -
_____
sock

**s** _____
bus

_____
- - - - - - - - - - - -
_____
saw

**Directions:** Name each picture. Write *s* if the word ends with /s/. Color the picture if the word begins with /s/.

**Home Activity:** Have your child find an object that begins with the letter *s*, draw a picture of it, and write the word.

School + Home

Name _____

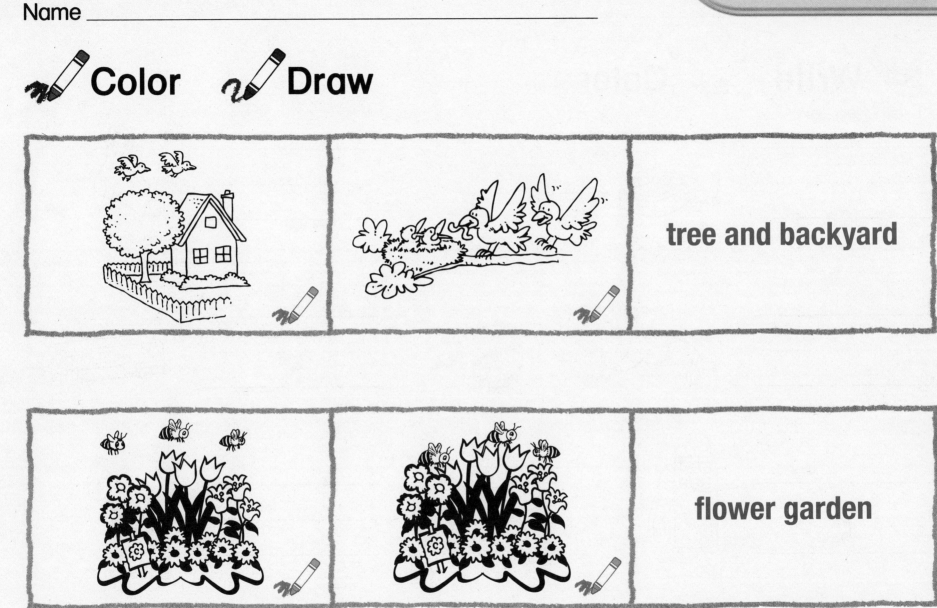

**Color**  **Draw**

tree and backyard

flower garden

**Directions:** Color the two pictures. Then in the last box draw a picture that tells where the story takes place.

 **Home Activity:** Have your child draw a picture of where the story takes place for one of his or her favorite stories.

Name _____

 **Read It!**

I see two mats.

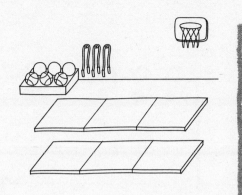

## Say It!

Say a sentence that tells about things you have.

✏️ **Write It!**

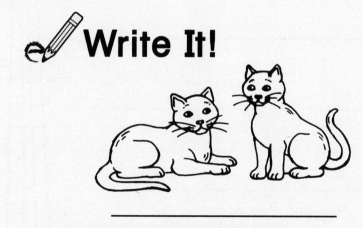

_____

I see two __cats__. (cats)

**Directions:** Have children read the sentence about the picture with you. Ask them to tell about things they have in a sentence. Then have children write a word that means more than one to complete the sentence.

 **School + Home** **Home Activity:** Ask your child to draw other pictures that show more than one.

Name _____

# ✏️ Write

**Answers will vary.**

1

2

3

**Directions:** Make a list of three things from the book that you want to learn more about.

**School + Home** **Home Activity:** Help your child write a list. It could be a grocery list or list of things to do.

**102 Writing List**

Name _____

# Color

 **Directions:** Color the picture that shows what comes first in each story.

 **Home Activity:** Have your child draw three pictures to show how to feed a pet.

Name _____

✏️ Circle  ✏️ Write  🖍️ Color

Mat
sat
(Mat)

Tam
mat
(Tam)

Sam
sat
(Sam)

 **Directions** Read the words and say the picture name. Circle the word that names the person in the picture. Then write the word and color the picture.

 **Home Activity** Help your child write the names for family members or friends and draw their pictures.

**104** **Conventions** Proper Nouns

Name _____

✏️ **Write**

P   P   P   P   P

p   p   p   p   p

Pam __Pam__

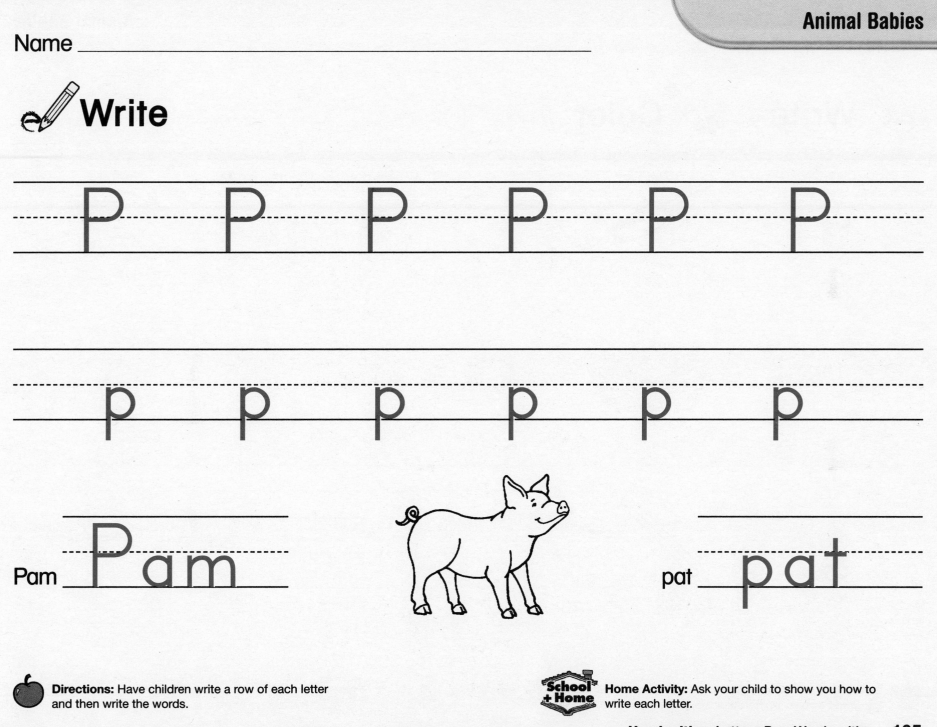

pat __pat__

🍎 **Directions:** Have children write a row of each letter and then write the words.

🏠 School + Home **Home Activity:** Ask your child to show you how to write each letter.

**Handwriting** Letters *P, p*: Words with *p*  **105**

Name _____

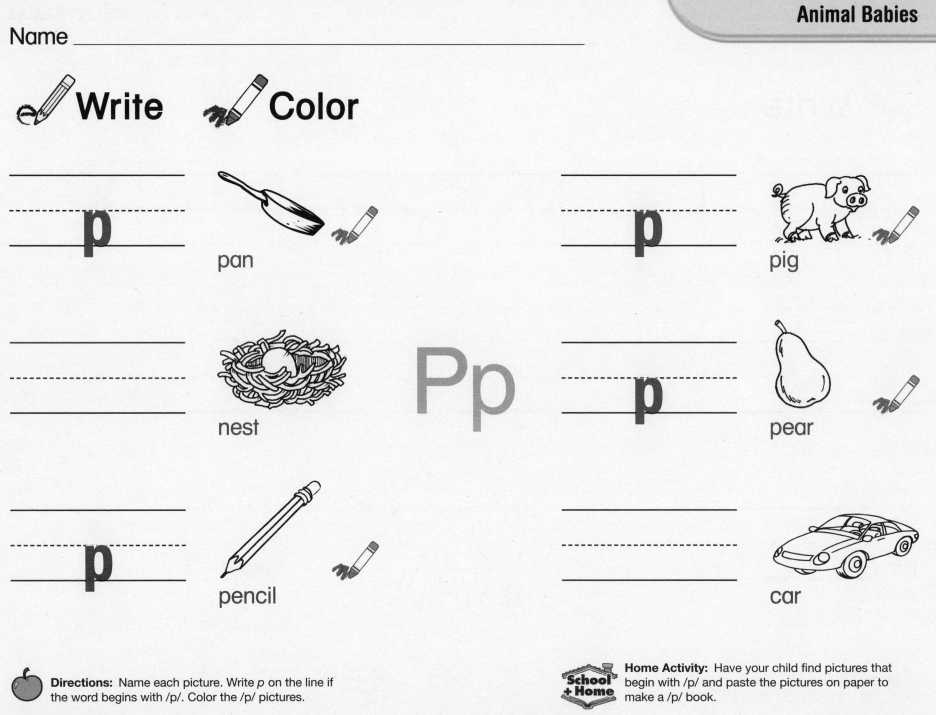

✏️ **Write**      🖍️ **Color**

p      pan

p      pig

nest      Pp

p      pear

p      pencil

car

**Directions:** Name each picture. Write *p* on the line if the word begins with /p/. Color the /p/ pictures.

© Pearson Education, Inc., K

**School + Home** **Home Activity:** Have your child find pictures that begin with /p/ and paste the pictures on paper to make a /p/ book.

# Pat the Cat

I like to pat my cat.

I like to pat Pam.

**Decodable Story** *Pat the Cat*
**Target Skill** /p/ Spelled *Pp*

I pat my cat, Pam.

We pat Pam.

Name _____

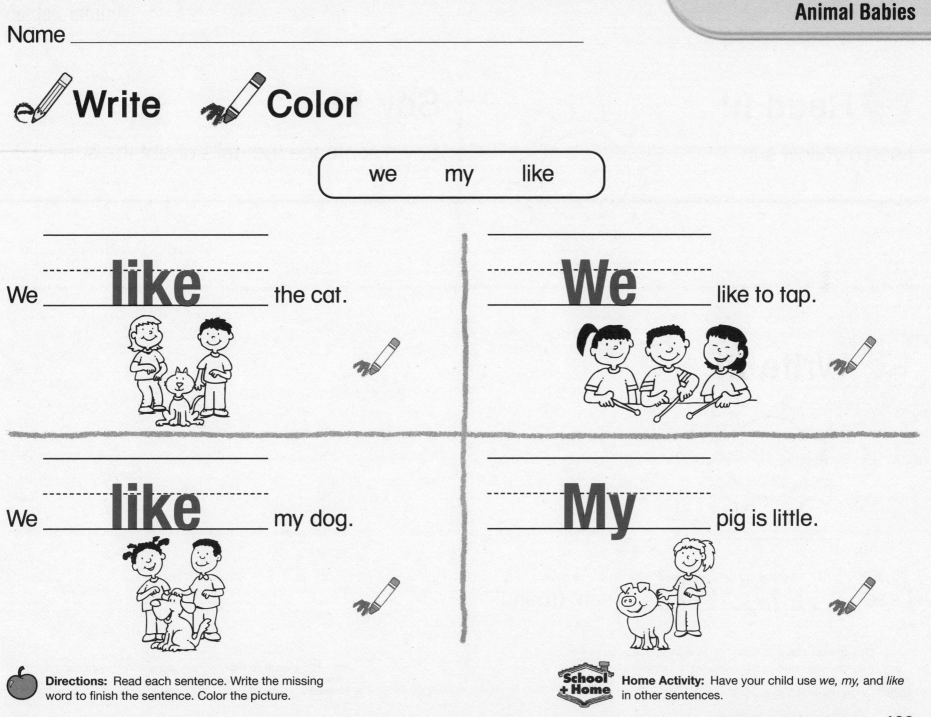

✏️ **Write**    🖍️ **Color**

we    my    like

_____
We **like** the cat.

_____
**We** like to tap.

_____
We **like** my dog.

_____
**My** pig is little.

🍎 **Directions:** Read each sentence. Write the missing word to finish the sentence. Color the picture.

**School + Home** **Home Activity:** Have your child use *we*, *my*, and *like* in other sentences.

Name _____

 **Read It!**

I see a yellow sun.

## Say It!

Say a sentence that tells about the sun.

 **Write It!**

_____

I see a _____ **round** _____ sun. (round)

**Directions:** Have children read the sentence about the sun. Ask them to say a sentence that tells about the sun. Then have children write the word that tells about the shape of the sun.

 **School + Home**

**Home Activity:** Show pictures to your child and have him or her use color words and shape words to describe items in the pictures.

**Conventions** Adjectives (Color and Shape)

Name _____

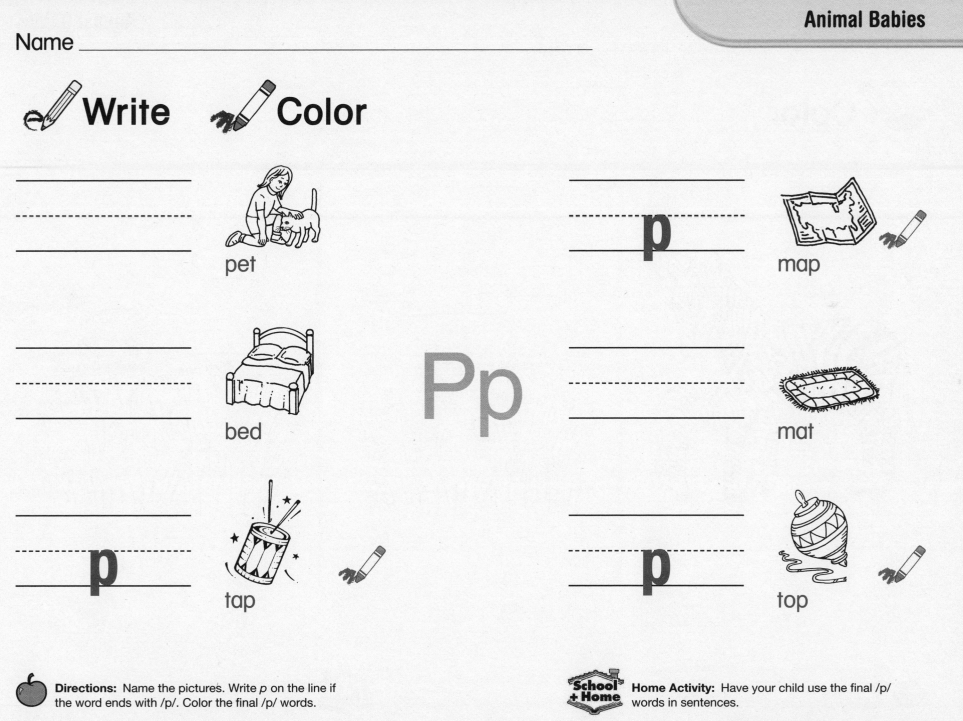

Write    Color

pet

bed

**p**    tap

**p**    map

mat

**p**    top

Pp

**Directions:** Name the pictures. Write *p* on the line if the word ends with /p/. Color the final /p/ words.

**Home Activity:** Have your child use the final /p/ words in sentences.

**Phonics** /p/ Spelled *Pp*    **111**

Name _____

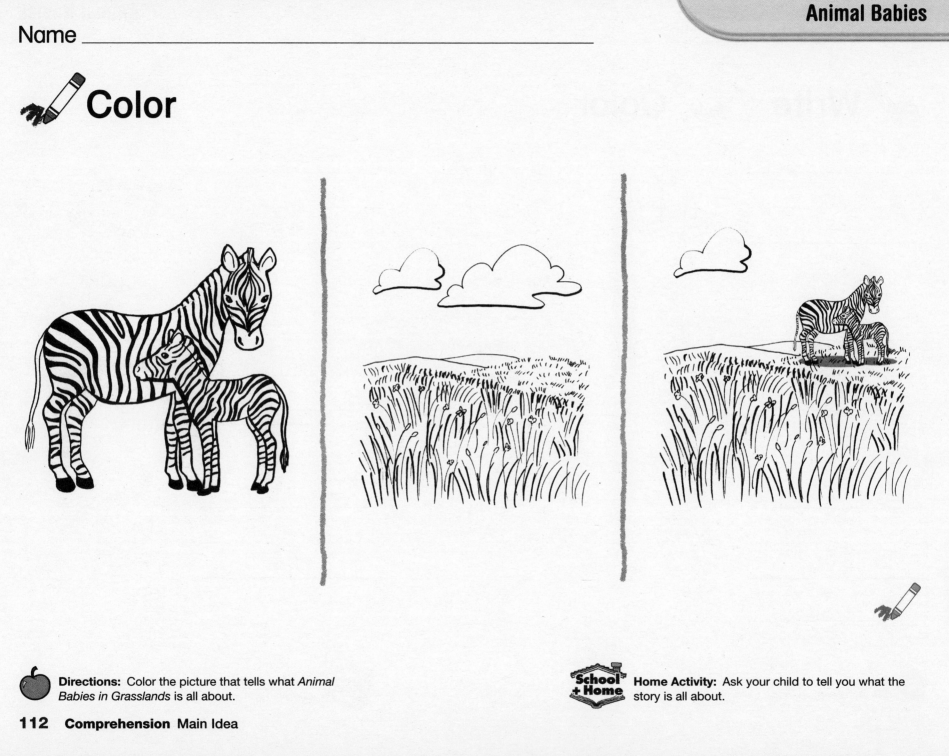

## Color

**Directions:** Color the picture that tells what *Animal Babies in Grasslands* is all about.

**School + Home** **Home Activity:** Ask your child to tell you what the story is all about.

Name _____

✏️ **Write**   🖍️ **Color**

Pam

Sam

Pat

Sam

Pat

Pam

 **Directions** Write the name under each picture.
Then color the pictures.

 **Home Activity** Help your child make a list of names
for pets and people.

Name _____

# ✏️ Write

trunk
big ears
tail

**Directions:** Write a note about something you want
to remember about the elephants.

 **Home Activity:** Have your child make some notes
about a favorite animal.

© Pearson Education, Inc., K

Name _____

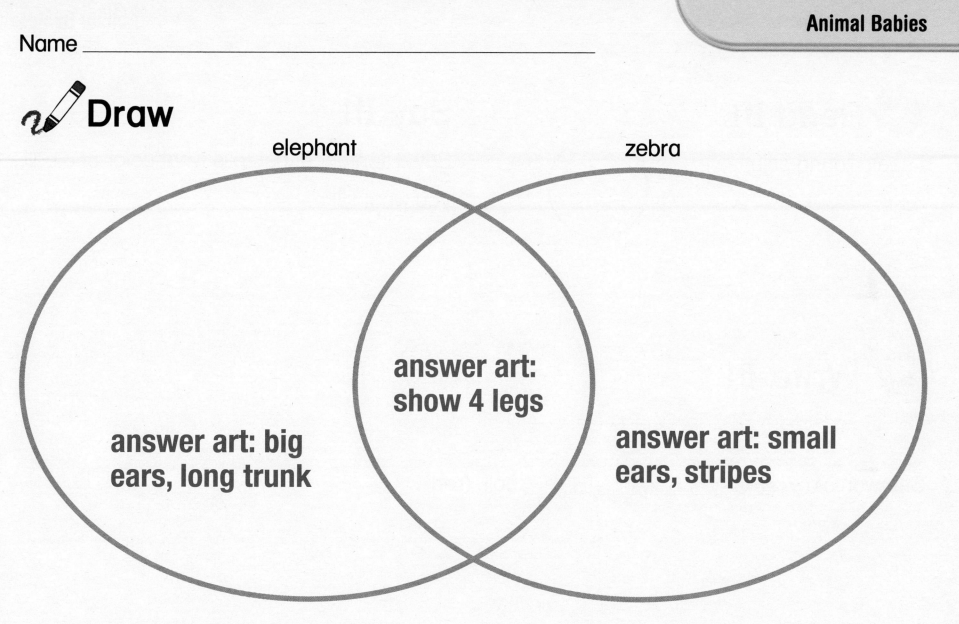

✐ **Draw**

elephant

zebra

answer art:
show 4 legs

answer art: big
ears, long trunk

answer art: small
ears, stripes

**Directions:** In the left and right circles, draw pictures
that show how the elephant and the zebra are
different. In the space in the middle, draw a picture
that shows how they are alike.

**Home Activity:** While you eat a meal together, talk
with your child about how the foods are alike and
different.

**Comprehension** Compare and Contrast **115**

Name _____

 ## Read It!

I see a round ball.

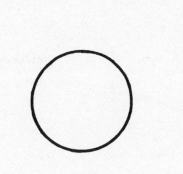

## Say It!

Say a sentence that tells what color of a ball you would like.

 ## Write It!

_____

- - - - - - - - - - - - - - - - - - - - - - - - - - - - - - -

She wants a **Answers will vary.** ball. (red)

© Pearson Education, Inc., K

**Directions:** Have children read the sentence about the ball. Ask them to give a sentence that tells the color of the ball they would like. Then have children write the color word to complete the sentence.

 **Home Activity:** Help your child match items of the same shape or color and tell about the item—*I see a square table. I see a square book.*

**116** **Conventions** Adjectives (Color and Shape)

Name _____

✏️ **Write**

C   C   C   C   C   C

c   c   c   c   c   c

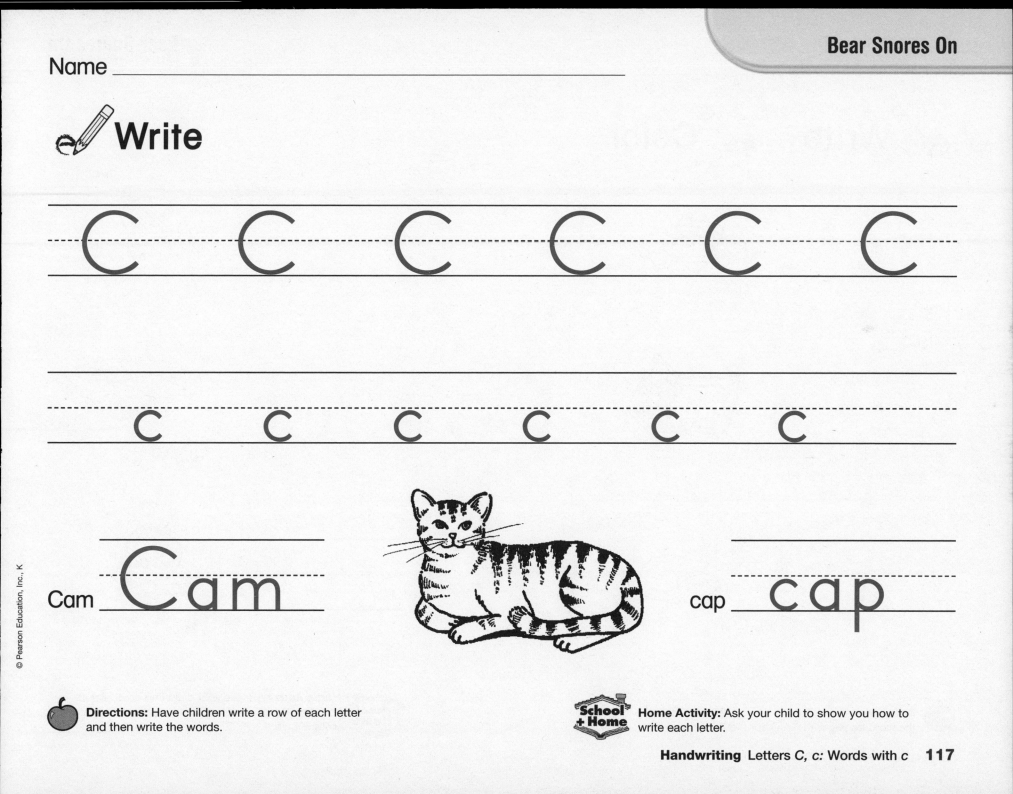

Cam   Cam

cap   cap

🍎 **Directions:** Have children write a row of each letter and then write the words.

**School + Home**   **Home Activity:** Ask your child to show you how to write each letter.

**Handwriting** Letters *C, c:* Words with *c*   **117**

Name _____

✏️ **Write**   🖍️ **Color**

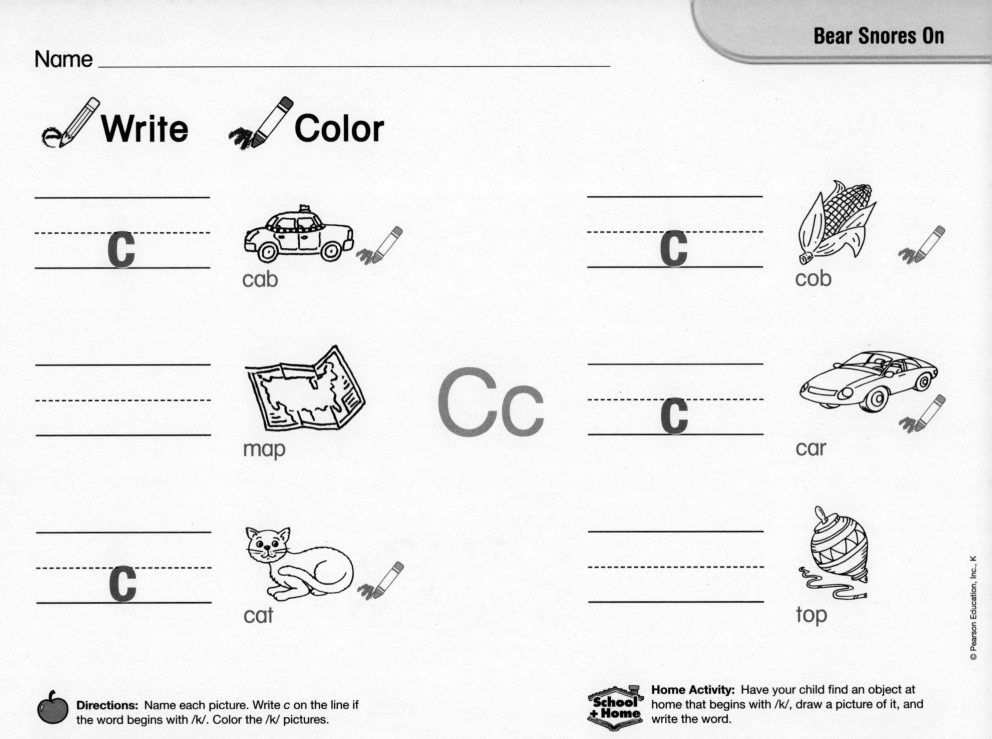

c

cab

c

cob

map

c

car

Cc

c

cat

top

**Directions:** Name each picture. Write *c* on the line if the word begins with /k/. Color the /k/ pictures.

**School + Home** **Home Activity:** Have your child find an object at home that begins with /k/, draw a picture of it, and write the word.

118   **Phonics** /k/ Spelled *Cc*

© Pearson Education, Inc., K

We like the caps.

# The Cap

I have a cap.

The cap is my cap.

I like my cap.

Name _____

✏ Write   🖍 Color

| we | my | like |

_____

It is ___ **my** ___ cat.

_____

___ **We** ___ have a cat.

_____

We ___ **like** ___ the cat.

_____

We like ___ **my** ___ cat.

**Directions:** Read each sentence. Write the missing word to finish the sentence. Color the picture.

**School + Home** **Home Activity:** Have your child use *we*, *my*, and *like* in other sentences.

© Pearson Education, Inc., K

**High-Frequency Words   121**

Name _____

 # Read It!

I see a big cap.

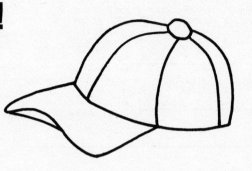

# Say It!

Say a sentence that tells about the caps.

 # Write It!

_____

I see two **little** caps. (little)

**Directions:** Have children read the sentence about the size of the cap. Ask them to give a sentence that tells about the caps. Then have children write the word that tells about the caps.

 **Home Activity:** Arrange pencils into groups by size. Have your child count and tell how many and what size.

**122** **Conventions** Adjectives (Size and Number)

Name _____

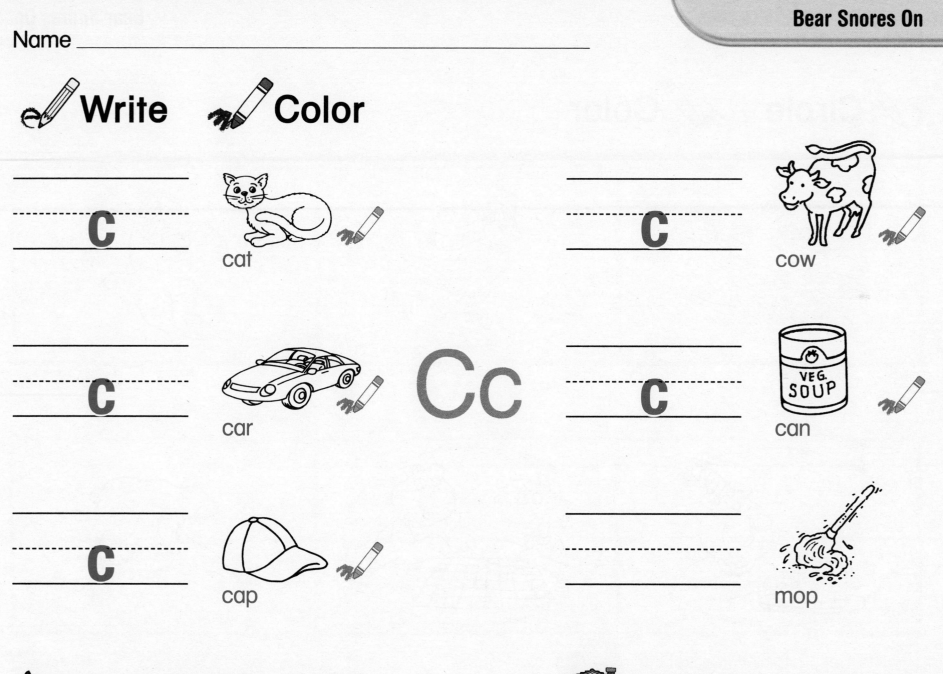

✏️ **Write**    🖍️ **Color**

_____
- - - - - - - - - - - - - - -
**c**
_____
cat

_____
- - - - - - - - - - - - - - -
**c**
_____
car

_____
- - - - - - - - - - - - - - -
**c**
_____
cap

**Cc**

_____
- - - - - - - - - - - - - - -
**c**
_____
cow

_____
- - - - - - - - - - - - - - -
**c**
_____
can

_____
_____
mop

🍎 **Directions:** Name each picture. Write *c* on the line if the word begins with /k/. Color the /k/ pictures.

 **Home Activity:** Have your child find other words that begin with /k/.

Name _____

 Circle　　 Color

**Directions:** Circle the make-believe pictures. Color the real pictures.

**School + Home** **Home Activity:** With your child, look at a book about how real animals live.

Name _____

 **Read It!**

I see a red book.

**Say It!**

Say a sentence that

tells about the hat.

 **Write It!**

_____

I see a _____ **round** _____ ball. (round)

**Directions:** Have children read the sentence that tells about the book. Ask them to give a sentence that tells about the hat. Then have children write the word that tells about the shape of the ball.

 **School + Home**

**Home Activity:** Have your child find things around the house that look like a circle, square, or triangle and tell about the shape and its color.

**Conventions** Adjectives (Color and Shape)  **125**

Name _____

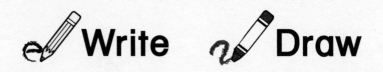 **Write** **Draw**

**Answers will vary**

© Pearson Education, Inc., K

**Directions:** Have children copy the class poem they wrote about the cat. Then have them draw a picture of a cat.

 **School + Home** **Home Activity:** Help your child make a poem with rhyming words such as *bat, cat. hat,* and *rat.*

Name _____

✏️ **Draw**   ✏️ **Write**

Answers will vary.

 **Directions:** Draw your favorite scene from *Bear Snores On.* Then write or dictate words describing where and when it happened.

 **Home Activity:** Talk about or look at photographs of a favorite event with your child. Discuss where and when it happened.

**Comprehension** Setting   **127**

Name _____

 # Read It!

I see two little cats.

# Say It!

Say a sentence that tells about the cats.

# Write It!

I see one _____ **big** _____ cat. (big)

 **Directions:** Have children read the sentence that tells about the size of the cats. Ask them to say a sentence that tells about the cats. Then have children write the word that tells about the cat.

 **Home Activity:** Gather a set of big and little books (or other items). Have your child choose the size and amount you say (1 little book).

**128** **Conventions** Adjectives (Size and Number)

© Pearson Education, Inc., K

Name _____

✏️ **Write**

I     I     I     I     I     I

i     i     i     i     i     i

in    in

it    it

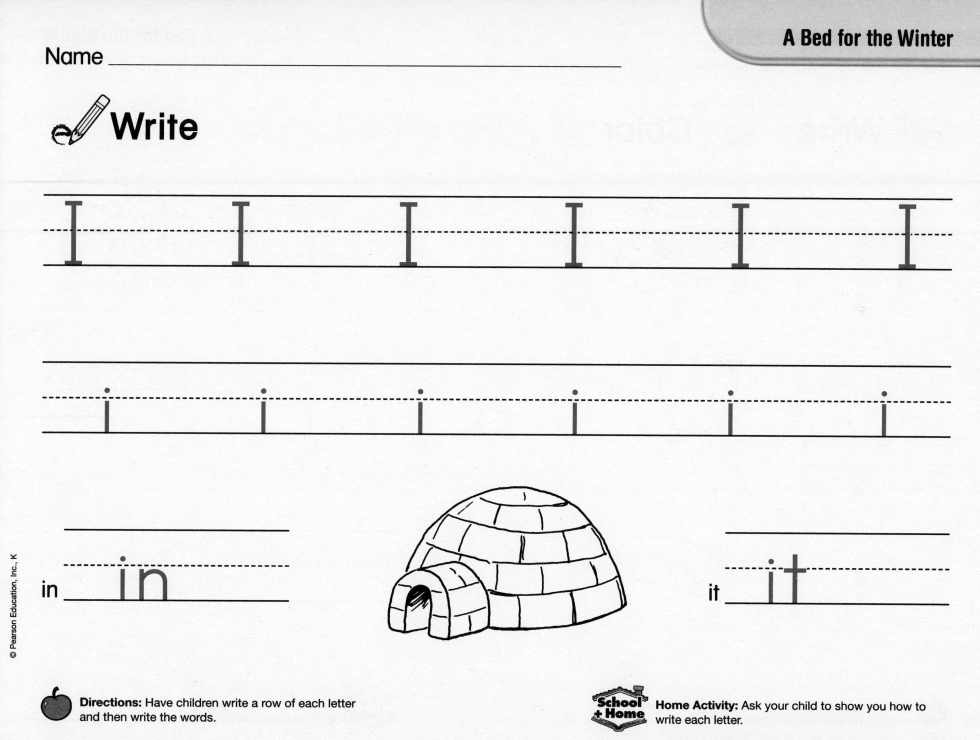

🍎 **Directions:** Have children write a row of each letter and then write the words.

🏠 **School + Home**   **Home Activity:** Ask your child to show you how to write each letter.

**Handwriting** Letters *I, i:* Words with *i*   **129**

Name _____

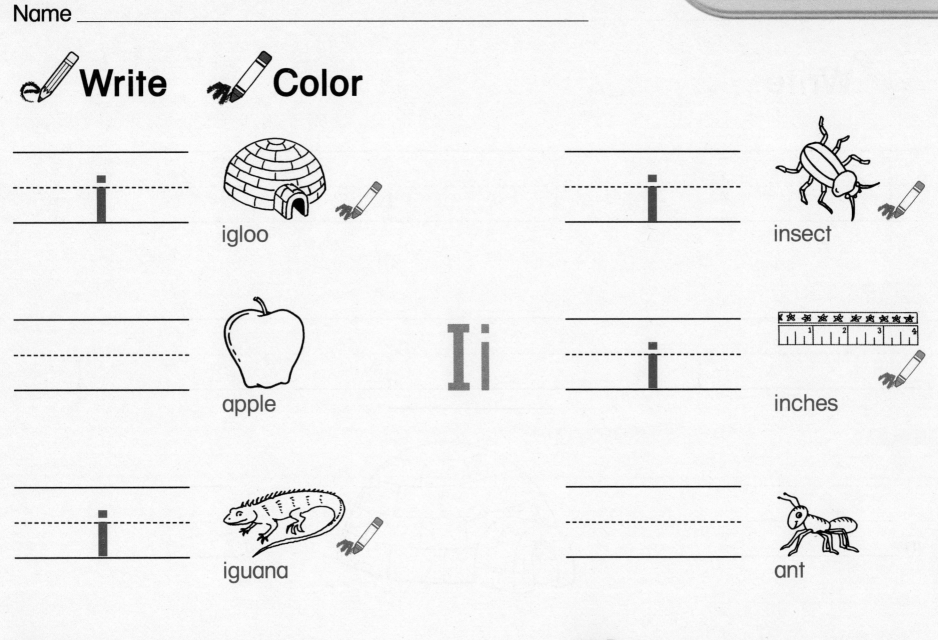

✏️ **Write**   🖍️ **Color**

igloo

apple

iguana

Ii

insect

inches

ant

🍎 **Directions:** Name each picture. Write *i* on the line if the word begins with /i/. Color the /i/ words.

🏠 **School + Home**   **Home Activity:** Look through a newspaper or book with your child and point out words that begin with *Ii*.

He is a little pig.

© Pearson Education, Inc., K

**Decodable Story** *Tim the Pig*
**Target Skill** */i/ Spelled Ii*

# Tim the Pig

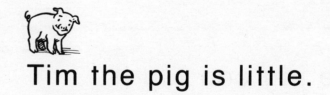

Tim the pig is little.

Tim the pig can tap it.

Tim the pig can pat it.

Name _____

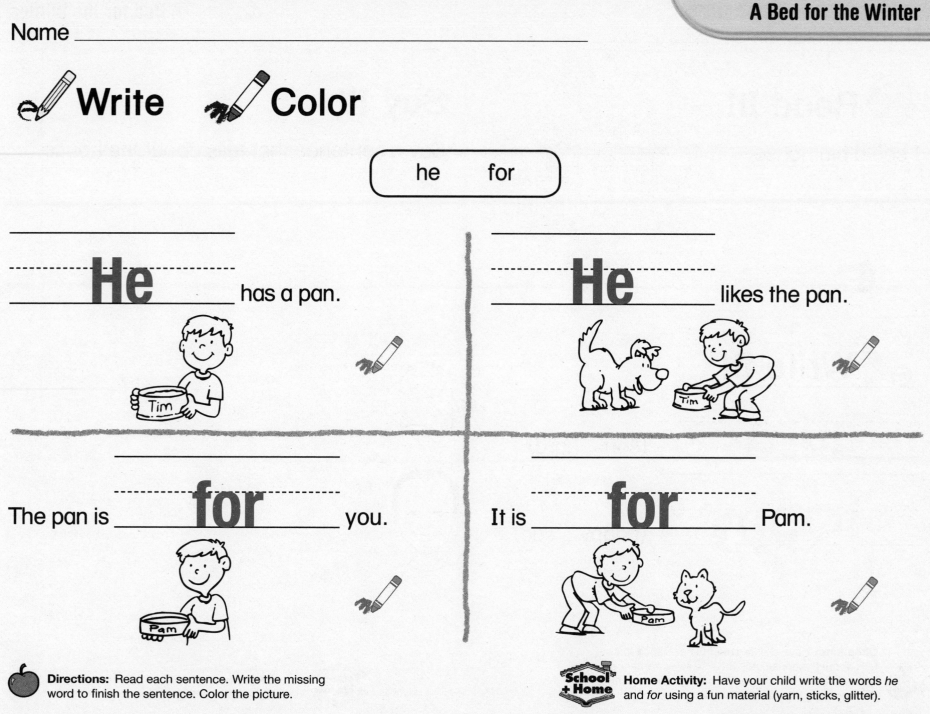

✏️ Write   🖍️ Color

| he    for |

_____
**He** ___ has a pan.

_____
**He** ___ likes the pan.

The pan is **for** ___ you.

It is **for** ___ Pam.

🍎 **Directions:** Read each sentence. Write the missing word to finish the sentence. Color the picture.

**School + Home**   **Home Activity:** Have your child write the words *he* and *for* using a fun material (yarn, sticks, glitter).

Name _____

 **Read It!**

I see a big house.

**Say It!**

Say a sentence that tells about the house.

**Write It!**

**hard** (soft    hard)

**happy** (happy    sad)

 **Directions:** Have children read the sentence that tells about the house. Ask them to say a sentence that tells about the house. Then have children write the word that tells about each picture.

 **Home Activity:** Ask your child to name the opposite of these words: *up, large, front, over.*

**134    Conventions** Adjectives (Opposites)

Name _____

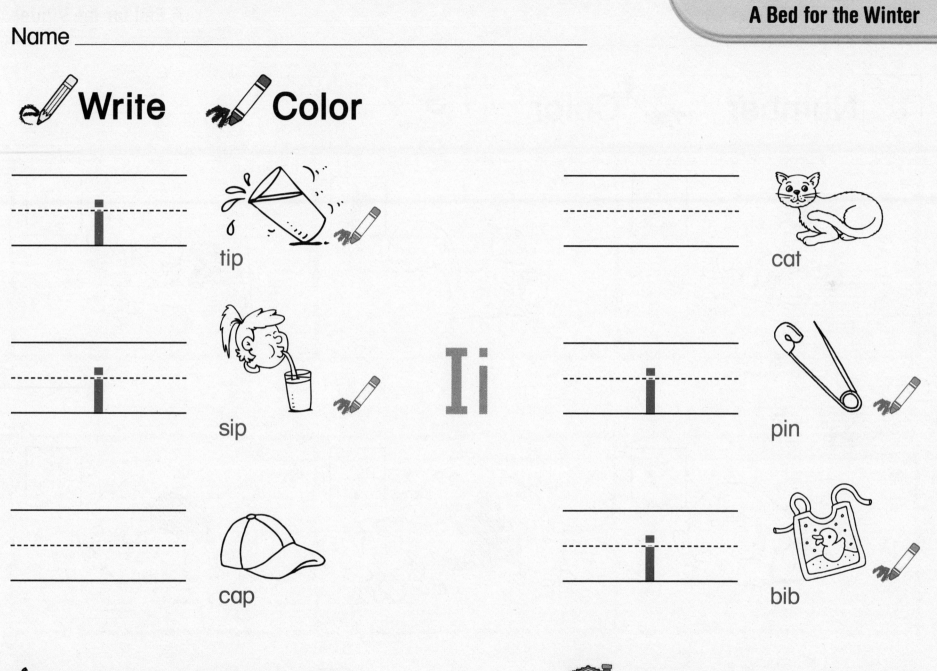

✏️ Write ✏️ Color

tip

sip

cap

Ii

cat

pin

bib

🍎 **Directions:** Name each picture. Write *i* on the line if the word has /i/ in the middle. Color the /i/ words.

 **School + Home** **Home Activity:** Help your child make a list of words with /i/.

Name _____

 Number ✏️ Color

 **Directions:** Number the pictures to show what happened first, next, and last. Color the pictures.

 **Home Activity:** Have your child tell the steps to make something.

Name _____

 **Read It!**

I see a big pig.

**Say It!**

Say a sentence that tells about the pigs.

 **Write It!**

I see two _____ **big** _____ pigs. (big)

**Directions:** Have children read the sentence that tells about the size of the pig. Ask them to say a sentence that tells about the pigs. Then have children write the word that tells about the pigs.

 **Home Activity:** Point to items in the house. Ask your child to name the size and number for the item.

Name _____

✏ Draw    ✏ Write

Answers will vary.

© Pearson Education, Inc., K

**Directions:** Draw a picture of an animal home. Then write a caption for your picture.

**School + Home**

**Home Activity:** Point to pictures in a book or magazine and have your child think of a caption for each picture.

Name _____

# ✏️ Color

 **Directions:** Color the items in each row that belong together.

 **Home Activity:** Name a category—animals, Ask your child to name things that fit the category.

**Comprehension** Classify and Categorize   **139**

© Pearson Education, Inc., K

Name _____

 **Read It!**

I see a little dog.

**Say It!**

Say a sentence that tells about the dog.

 **Write It!**

_____

**tall** (tall   short)

_____

**open** (shut   open)

 **Directions:** Have children read the sentence that tells about the dog. Ask them to say a sentence that tells about the dog. Ask children to write the word that tells about the picture on each line.

**School + Home** **Home Activity:** Have your child say the opposite of a word you name. Use words such as *up, back, over,* and *sad.*

© Pearson Education, Inc., K

Name _____

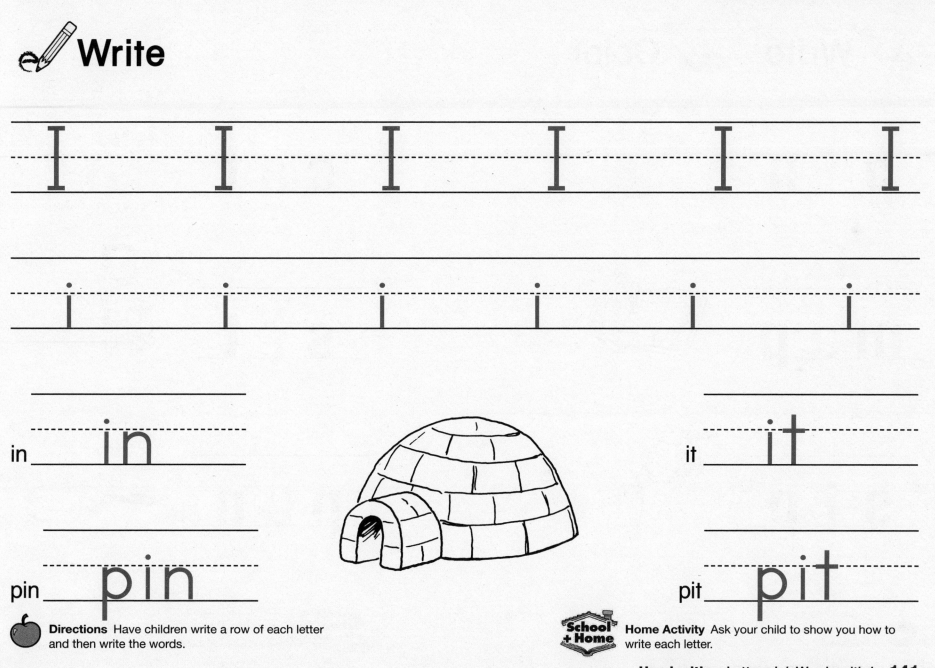

✏️ **Write**

I   I   I   I   I   I   I

i   i   i   i   i   i

in ___in___

it ___it___

pin ___pin___

pit ___pit___

**Directions** Have children write a row of each letter and then write the words.

**School + Home** **Home Activity** Ask your child to show you how to write each letter.

Name _____

✏️ Write   🖍️ Color

pin

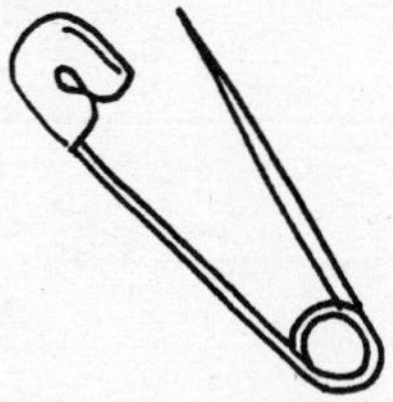

cat

map

sit

sip

pan

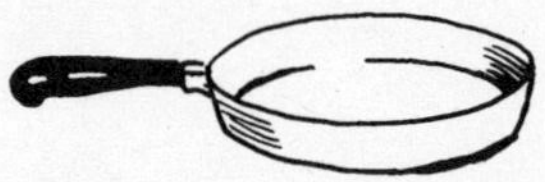

🍎 **Directions:** Write *i* or *a* to finish each word. Color the /i/ pictures.

**School + Home** **Home Activity:** Have your child write *tip* and *tap* and draw a picture for each word.

Sit, pat, sip.

**4**

# Sam, Sit!

Sam, sit.

**1**

Sam, pat.

Sam, sip.

Name _____

# ✏️ Draw

| Idea 1 | Idea 2 | Idea 3 |
|--------|--------|--------|
| Pictures will vary. | | |

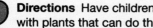 **Directions** Have children draw pictures of children with plants that can do things real plants cannot.

 **Home Activity** Ask your child to tell you about what is happening in the pictures.

© Pearson Education, Inc., K

Name _____

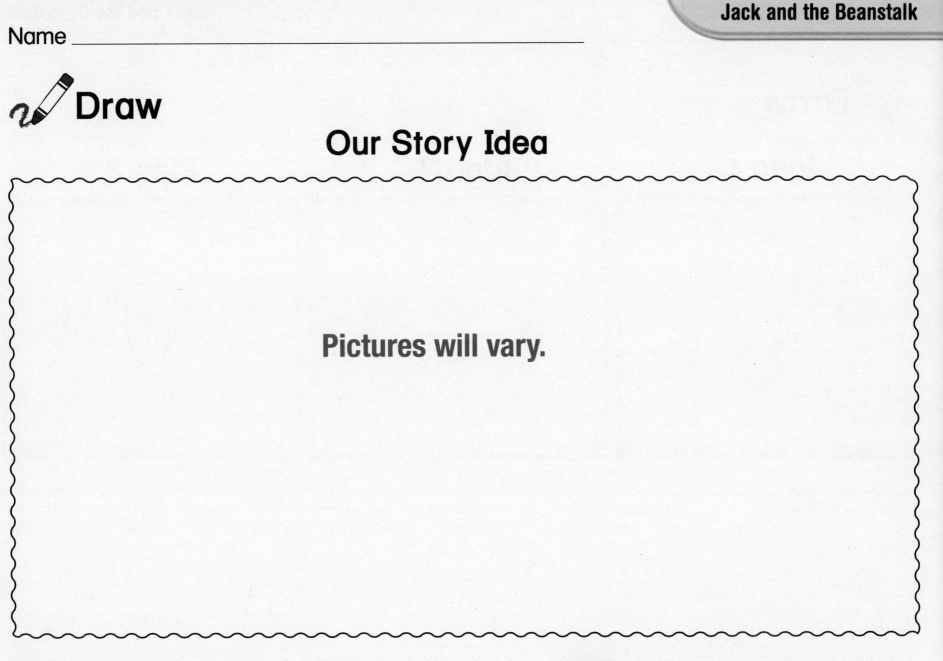

# Draw

## Our Story Idea

Pictures will vary.

 **Directions** Have children draw a picture of the class's story idea.

**School + Home** **Home Activity** Ask your child to tell you how the picture shows the class's story idea.

Name _____

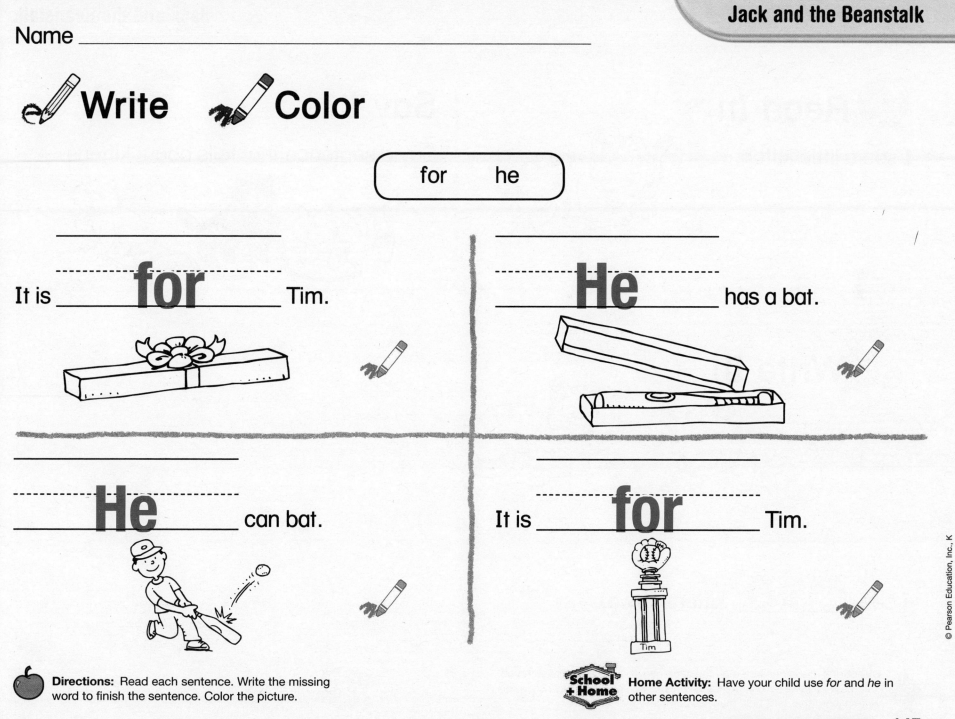

✏️ **Write**   🖍️ **Color**

for          he

_____
It is _____ **for** _____ Tim.

_____
**He** _____ has a bat.

_____
**He** _____ can bat.

_____
It is _____ **for** _____ Tim.

**Directions:** Read each sentence. Write the missing word to finish the sentence. Color the picture.

**School + Home**  **Home Activity:** Have your child use *for* and *he* in other sentences.

Name _____

 # Read It!

I see a little kitten.

# Say It!

Say a sentence that tells about kittens.

 # Write It!

_____

I see **two** kittens. (two)

 **Directions** Have children read the sentence about the picture with you. Ask them to say a sentence that tells about kittens. Then have children write a word that tells how many to complete the sentence.

**School + Home** **Home Activity** Ask your child to name the color, shape, or size of things around the house.

Name _____

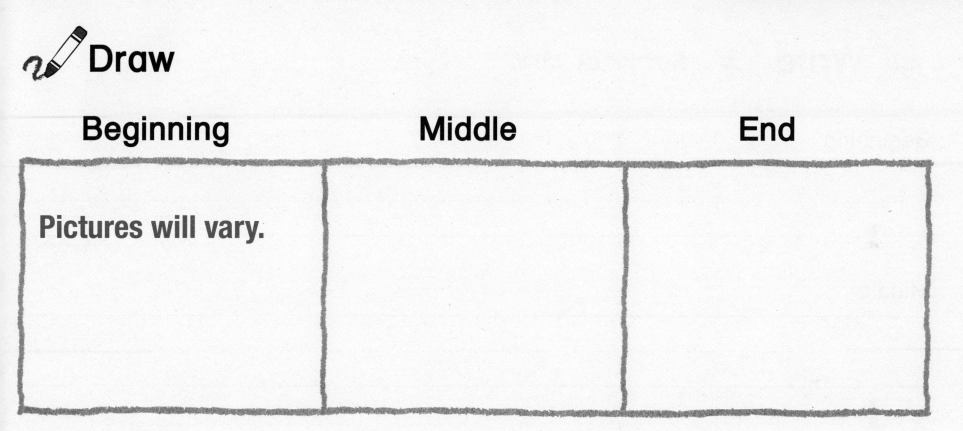

## ✏️ Draw

| Beginning | Middle | End |
|---|---|---|
| Pictures will vary. | | |

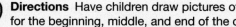 **Directions** Have children draw pictures of the events for the beginning, middle, and end of the class story.

 **School + Home** **Home Activity** Have your child tell about the sequence of events in the story.

Name _____

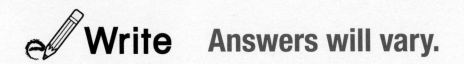 **Write**   **Answers will vary.**

**Beginning**

_____

- - - - - - - - - - - - - - - - - - - - - - - - - - - - - - - - - - - - - - - -

_____

**Middle**

_____

- - - - - - - - - - - - - - - - - - - - - - - - - - - - - - - - - - - - - - - -

_____

**End**

_____

- - - - - - - - - - - - - - - - - - - - - - - - - - - - - - - - - - - - - - - -

_____

 **Directions** Have children write or dictate words or sentences that tell the beginning, middle, and end of the class story.

 **School + Home** **Home Activity** Ask your child to read the words or sentences to you.

Name _____

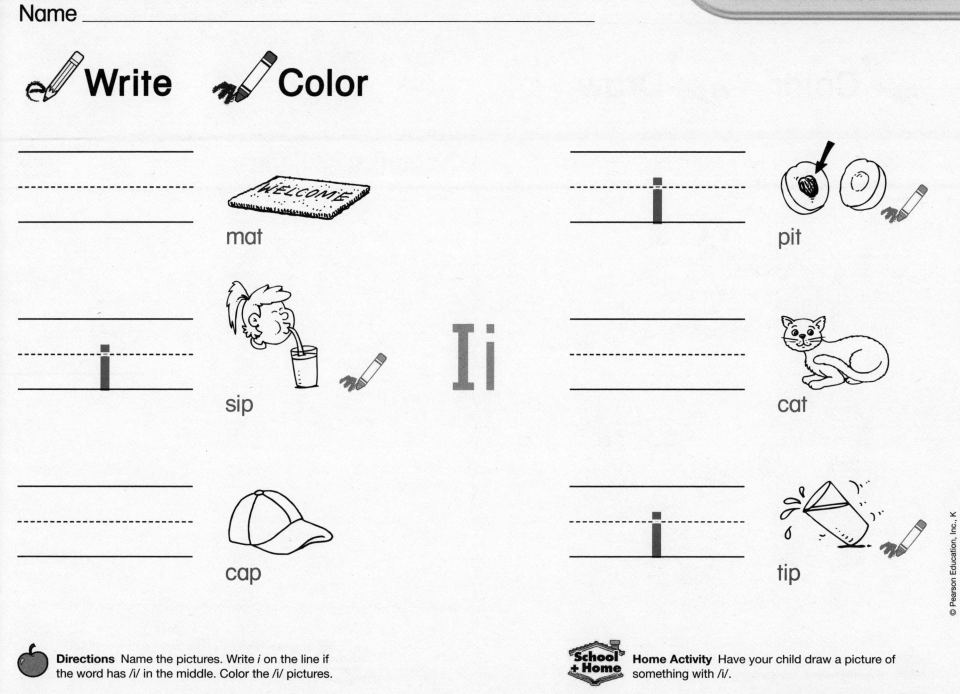

✏️ **Write**   🖍️ **Color**

mat

sip

cap

Ii

pit

cat

tip

🍎 **Directions** Name the pictures. Write *i* on the line if the word has /i/ in the middle. Color the /i/ pictures.

**School + Home** **Home Activity** Have your child draw a picture of something with /i/.

Name _____

 Color  Draw

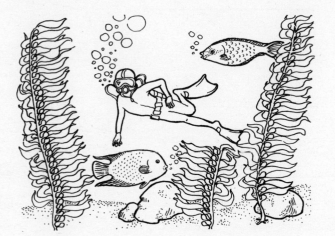

**Answers will vary.**

© Pearson Education, Inc., K

 **Directions** Color the picture that shows something make-believe. Draw something real in the box.

 **Home Activity** Read a favorite story with your child and talk about whether the story is make-believe or could really happen.

**152** **Comprehension** Realism and Fantasy

Name _____

#  Read It!

I see the hot sun.

# Say It!

Say a sentence that

tells about something

cold.

# 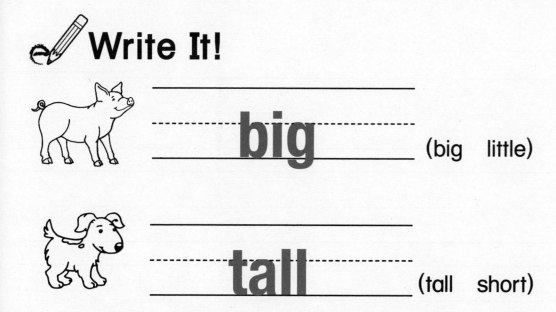 Write It!

big  (big   little)

tall  (tall   short)

**Directions** Have children read the sentence that tells about the sun. Ask them to say a sentence that tells about something cold. Then ask children to say the picture name and read the words together. Have them write the word that tells about each picture.

 **School + Home** **Home Activity** Ask your child to name the opposite of these words: *light, day, small, down.*

© Pearson Education, Inc., K

**Conventions** Adjectives (Opposites)  **153**

Name _____

✓ Draw   ✓ Write

## Details to Add

| Answers will vary. | | |
|---|---|---|

_____

- - - - - - - - - - - - - - - - - - - - - - - - - -

_____

- - - - - - - - - - - - - - - - - - - - - - - - - -

_____

- - - - - - - - - - - - - - - - - - - - - - - - - -

_____

**Directions** Have children draw pictures or write words or sentences with details about the class story.

**School + Home** **Home Activity** Ask your child to explain how the details can be added to the story.

Name _____

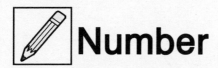 Number

**Directions** Number the pictures in each row to tell what happened first, next, and last.

**Home Activity** Help your child tell about things he or she did, noting what happened in order.

**Comprehension** Sequence **155**

Name _____

 # Read It!

This is a little book.

# Say It!

Say a sentence that tells about another book.

 # Write It!

_____

This is a ___**little**___ mouse. (little)

**Directions** Have children read the sentence about the picture with you. Ask them to give a sentence that tells about a book. Then have children write the word that tells about the size of the mouse to complete the sentence.

 **School + Home** **Home Activity** Choose other words and have your child use the words to describe something.

**156** **Conventions** Adjectives

Name _____

✏️ Circle   ✏️ Write

1. (Look) at that (plant).

_____

- - - - - - - - - - - - - - - - - - -

_____

2. (That is) a (fastjig).

_____

- - - - - - - - - - - - - - - - - - -

_____

3. (Thegirl) (has fun).

_____

- - - - - - - - - - - - - - - - - - -

_____

🍎 **Directions** Have children circle the mistakes and rewrite the words or sentences correctly on the lines.

 **Home Activity** Ask your child to explain why correct spacing between letters and words is important.

Name _____

 # Write

_____

Answers will vary.

**Directions** Have children copy the story sentences using correct spacing between letters and words.

 **School + Home** **Home Activity** Help your child edit the sentences by checking for correct letter and word spacing.

Name _____

✏️ Draw   ✏️ Write

Answers will vary.

Title: _____

Author: _____

**Directions** Have children draw a picture for a cover for their story. Help them write the story's title and their name.

**School + Home**   **Home Activity** Have your child explain how the picture and title go with the story.

© Pearson Education, Inc., K

Name _____

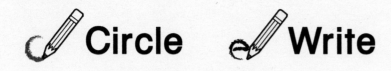 Circle   Write

I shared my story with _____ **Answers will vary.** _____.

Here's what he/she thought about my story.

_____

_____

_____

_____

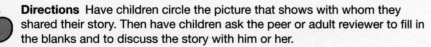 **Directions** Have children circle the picture that shows with whom they shared their story. Then have children ask the peer or adult reviewer to fill in the blanks and to discuss the story with him or her.

 **Home Activity** Ask your child to read or tell the class story to you.

Name _____

✏️ **Write**

N   N   N   N   N   N

n   n   n   n   n   n

Nan **Nan**

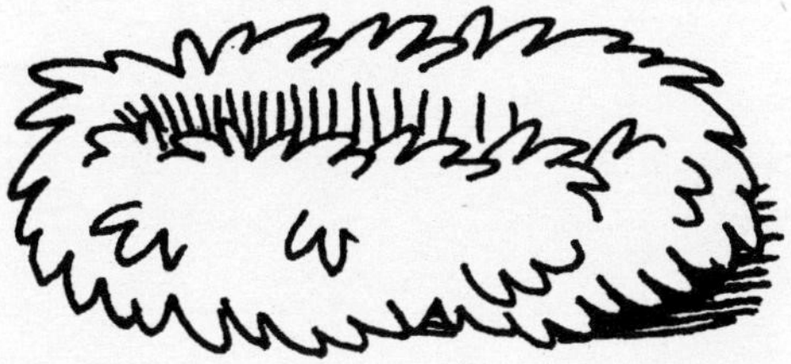

pan **pan**

**Directions:** Have children write a row of each letter and then write the words.

**School + Home**

**Home Activity:** Ask your child to write each letter and tell you how to make the letter.

Name _____

✏️ **Write**　🖍️ **Color**

n — nest

n — net

— pan

n — nose

— hen

n — nine

Nn

**Directions:** Name each picture. Write *n* on the line if the word begins with /n/. Color the /n/ pictures.

**School + Home**

**Home Activity:** Have your child name other words that begin with /n/.

Nat sat.

Nan sat with Nat.

**Decodable Story** *Nan and Nat*
**Target Skill** /n/ Spelled *Nn*

# Nan and Nat

I am Nan.

I am Nat.

We have nets.

Nan is with Nat.

Nat can nab with a net.

2

Nat nabs with the net.

Nan nabs with the net.

3

Name _____

✏️ **Write**    🖍️ **Color**

| she | with | me | we |

_____

Pam ran ___ **with** ___ me.

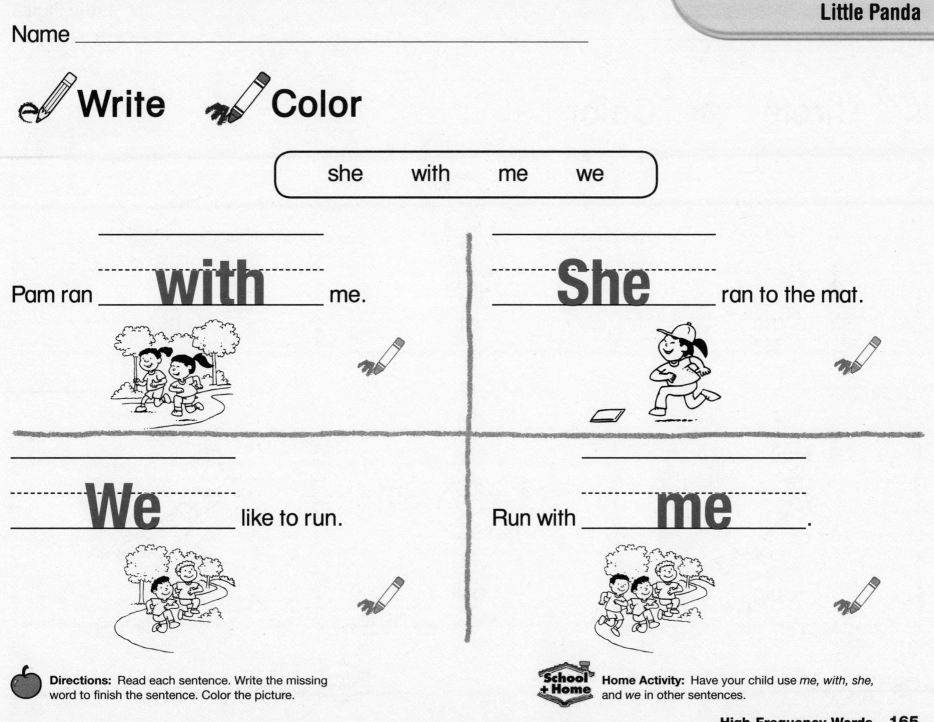

_____

___ **She** ___ ran to the mat.

_____

___ **We** ___ like to run.

_____

Run with ___ **me** ___.

🍎 **Directions:** Read each sentence. Write the missing word to finish the sentence. Color the picture.

🏫 **School + Home**    **Home Activity:** Have your child use *me, with, she,* and *we* in other sentences.

Name _____

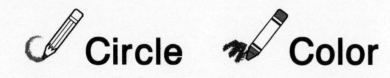 **Circle** **Color**

run

sit

net

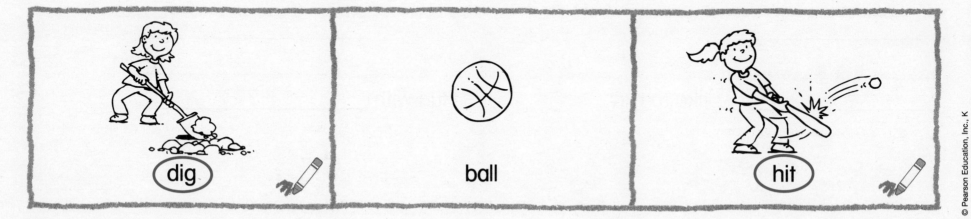

dig

ball

hit

🍎 **Directions** Name the pictures. Circle each verb and color the picture. Then use each verb in a sentence.

 **Home Activity** Have your child name other verbs.

Name _____

 **Write**    **Color**

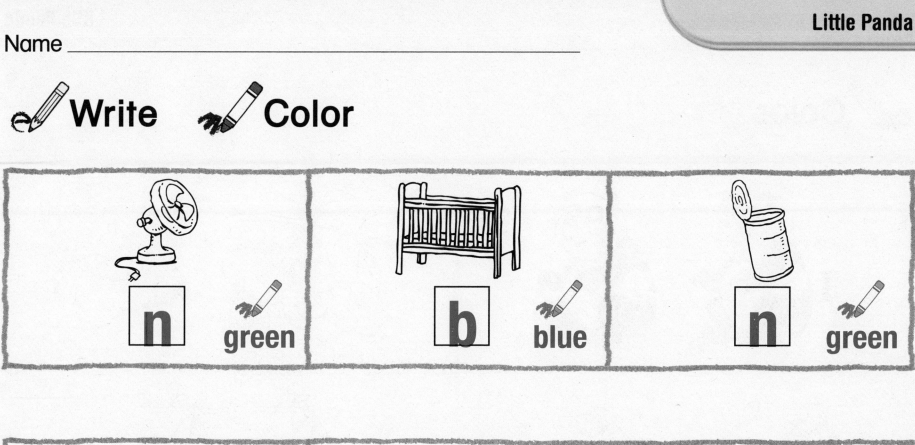

**n** green

**b** blue

**n** green

**b** blue

**n** green

**b** blue

**Directions:** Name each picture. Write the letter for the final sound in the box. Color final /n/ words green and final /b/ words blue.

 **School + Home** **Home Activity:** Have your child trace *n* and *b* and name the pictures.

Name _____

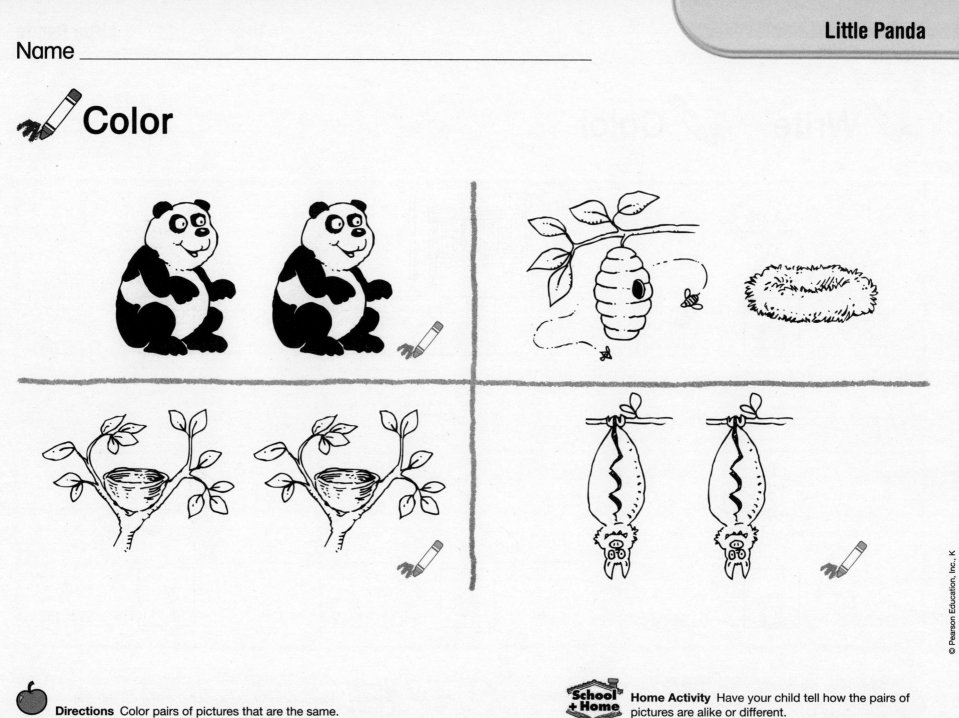

# Color

**Comprehension** Compare and Contrast

**Directions** Color pairs of pictures that are the same.

**Home Activity** Have your child tell how the pairs of pictures are alike or different.

Name _____

 **Read It!**

I see a little dog.

**Say It!**

Say a sentence that tells about dogs.

 **Write It!**

_____

I see a _____ **white** _____ cat. (white)

**Directions** Have children track the print and read the sentence with you. Ask them to say a sentence that tells about dogs. Then have children write an adjective to complete the sentence.

 **School + Home** **Home Activity** Have your child describe things they see at home, telling about the size, color, and number.

Name _____

 Draw  Write

Answers will vary.

_____

- - - - - - - - - - - - - - - - - - - - - - - - - - - - -

_____

_____

- - - - - - - - - - - - - - - - - - - - - - - - - - - - -

_____

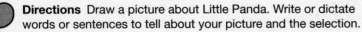 **Directions** Draw a picture about Little Panda. Write or dictate words or sentences to tell about your picture and the selection.

 **Home Activity** Help your child summarize events that happened at school or at home.

Name _____

 **Draw**

Answers will vary.

 **Directions** Draw a picture that shows what *Little Panda* is all about.

 **Home Activity:** Talk about several familiar stories and have your child tell you what each story is all about.

**Comprehension** Main Idea **171**

Name _____

✏ Circle    ✏ Write

(pat)
pit

**pat**

tap
(tip)

**tip**

(nap)
pin

**nap**

tan
(sit)

**sit**

🍎 **Directions** Say the picture name. Circle the word that tells the action. Then write the word. Use each word you wrote in a sentence.

**School + Home** **Home Activity** Ask your child to use the words that were not circled in sentences.

**172** **Conventions** Verbs

Name _____

✏️ **Write**

R R R R R R

r r r r r r

Rin **Rin**

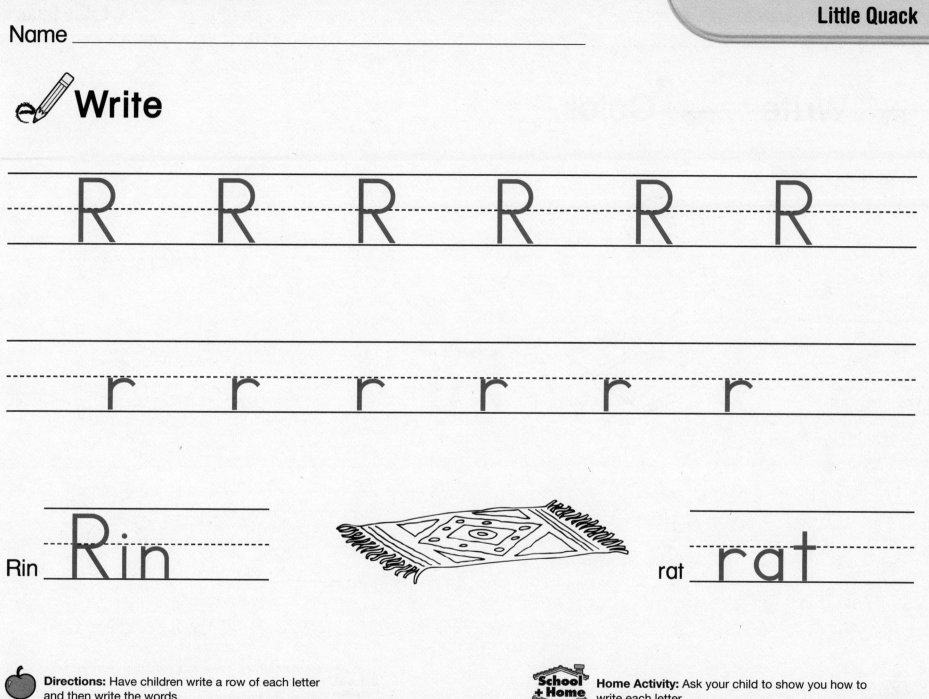

rat **rat**

🍎 **Directions:** Have children write a row of each letter and then write the words.

🏫 **School + Home** **Home Activity:** Ask your child to show you how to write each letter.

Name _____

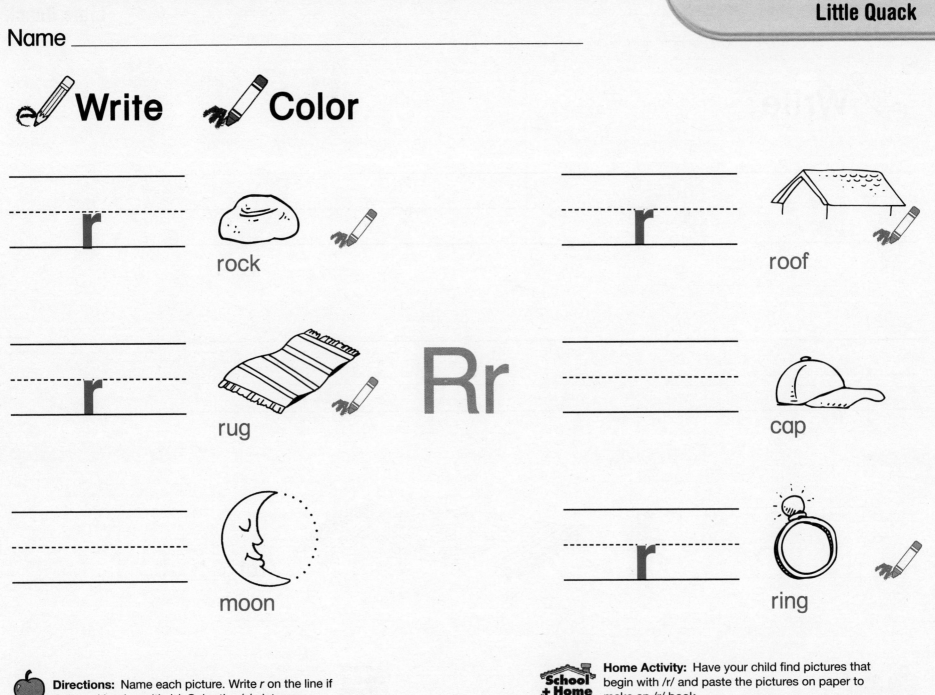

✏️ **Write**　　🖍️ **Color**

rock

rug

Rr

moon

roof

cap

ring

🍎 **Directions:** Name each picture. Write *r* on the line if the word begins with /r/. Color the /r/ pictures.

🏠 **School + Home**　**Home Activity:** Have your child find pictures that begin with /r/ and paste the pictures on paper to make an /r/ book.

Rin ran to Rip.

Rip ran.

4

# Rin the Rat

Rin is a rat.

She is a little rat.

1

Rin likes to tap.

She can tap.

Rip ran to Rin.

He is with Rin.

Name _____

✏️ **Write**    🖍️ **Color**

| she | with | me | little |

_____
**She** _____ can jump rope.

_____
She can run **with** _____ me.

_____
She can hop with **me** _____ .

_____
This is a **little** _____ duck.

🍎 **Directions:** Read each sentence. Write the missing word to finish the sentence. Color the picture.

School + Home **Home Activity:** Have your child use *she*, *with*, *little*, and *me* in other sentences.

Name _____

## Read It!

Tim jumps.

Tim jumped.

## Say It!

Say a sentence that tells something Tim is doing now. Then say a sentence that tells something Tim did yesterday.

## Write It!

Pam ____**walks**____. (walks)

 **Directions** Have children read the sentences about Tim. Ask them to give sentences for things Tim does now and did yesterday. Then have children write the word that completes the sentence about Pam.

 **Home Activity** Ask your child to tell about something he or she did today and then about something he or she did yesterday.

Name _____

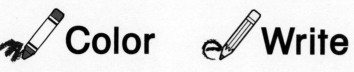 **Color** ✏️ **Write**

bed

rose
r

rug
r

rake
r

rhino
r

duck

rabbit
r

raccoon
r

 **Directions:** Color each picture that begins with /r/. Write *r* in the box.

 **School + Home**

**Home Activity:** Have your child name the pictures that begin with /r/.

**Phonics** /r/ Spelled *Rr* **179**

Name _____

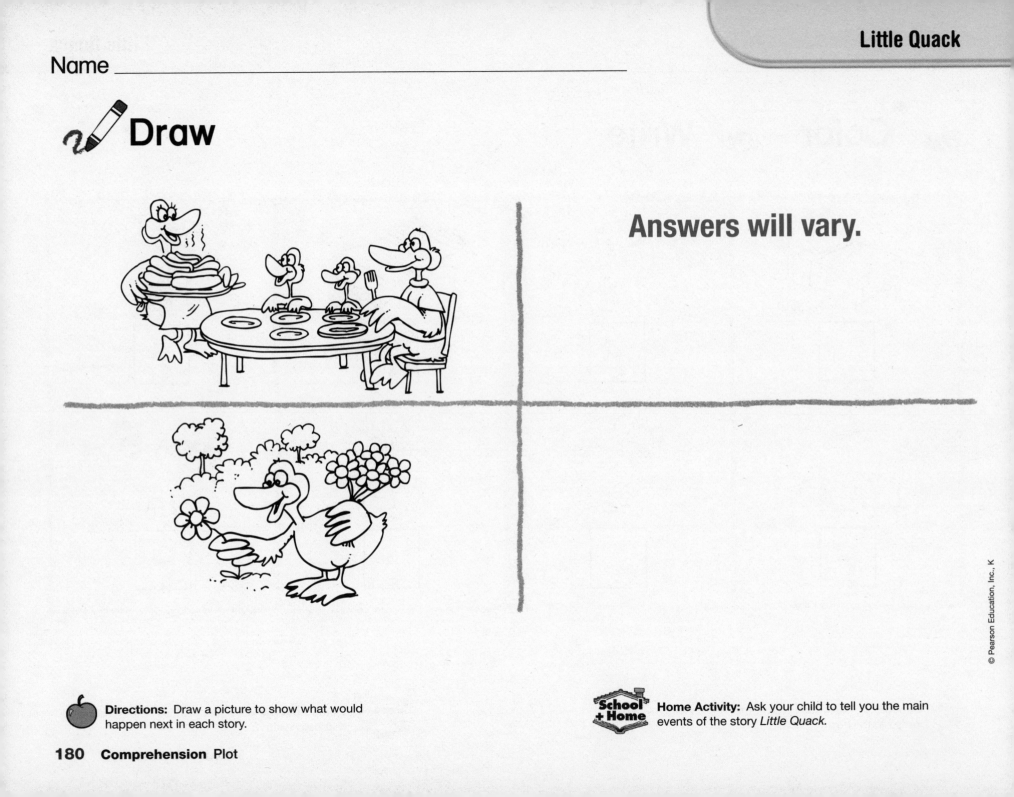

**Draw**

**Answers will vary.**

**Directions:** Draw a picture to show what would happen next in each story.

**Home Activity:** Ask your child to tell you the main events of the story *Little Quack*.

Name _____

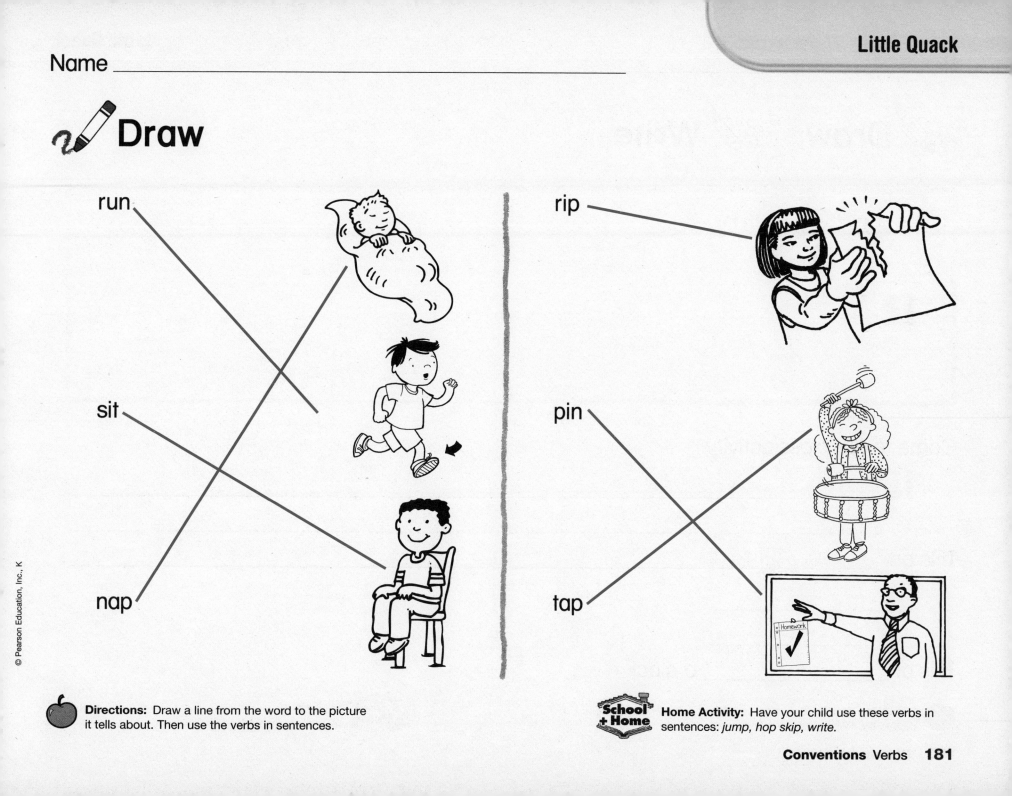

# ✎ Draw

run

sit

nap

rip

pin

tap

**Directions:** Draw a line from the word to the picture it tells about. Then use the verbs in sentences.

**School + Home**

**Home Activity:** Have your child use these verbs in sentences: *jump, hop skip, write.*

Name _____

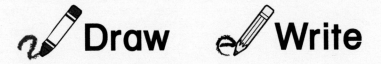 **Draw** **Write**

> Answers will vary.

Come to our class activity.

_____

- - - - - - - - - - - - - - - - - - - - - - - - - - - - - - - - - - - - - - - - - -

It is on _____.

_____

- - - - - - - - - - - - - - - - - - - - -

It is at _____ o'clock.

 **Directions** Draw a picture for your class activity. Then write or dictate the missing information for an invitation.

 **Home Activity** Help your child create an invitation to a real or make believe family event.

Name _____

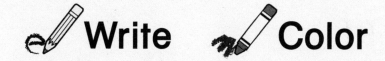 Write  Color

M

R

M

M

M

R

 **Directions:** Label the animal in each picture *R* for real or *M* for make-believe. Color the pictures that show a make-believe situation.

 **School + Home** **Home Activity:** Have your child draw and color a picture of a real animal in a real place.

**Comprehension** Realism and Fantasy **183**

Name _____

## Read It!

Nan talks.

Nan talked.

## Say It!

Say a sentence that tells something Nan is doing now. Then say a sentence that tells something Nan did yesterday.

## Write It!

Rob . (jumped)

**Directions** Have children read the sentences about Nan. Ask them to give sentences for things Nan does now and did yesterday. Then have children write the word that completes the sentence about Rob.

 **Home Activity** Have your child create other sentences about the pictures.

Name _____

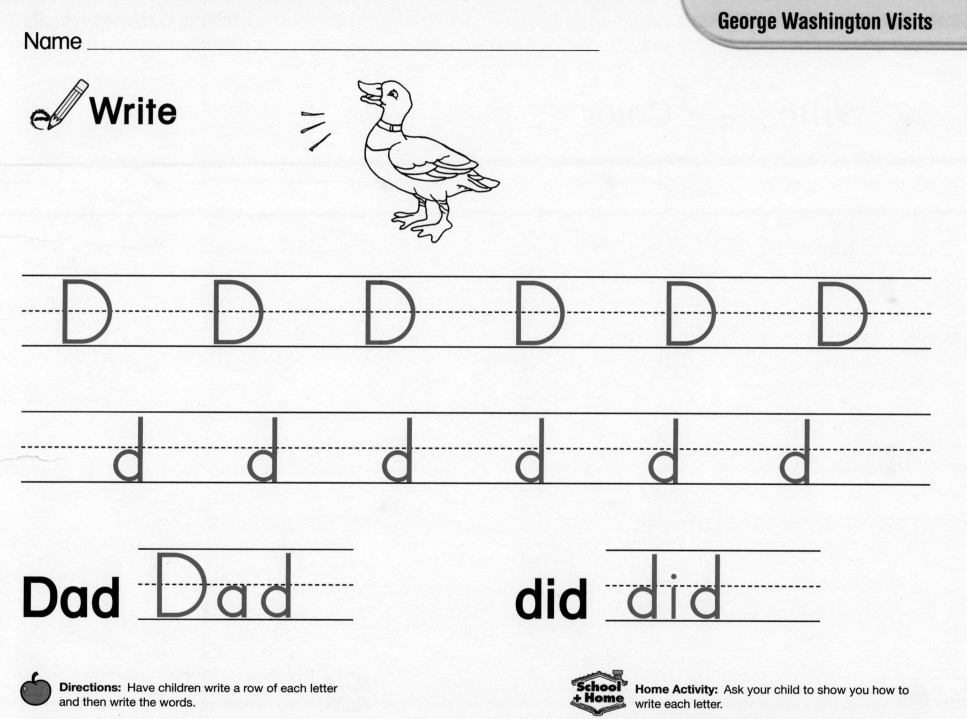

✏️ **Write**

D D D D D

d d d d d d

**Dad** Dad

**did** did

🍎 **Directions:** Have children write a row of each letter and then write the words.

🏫 School + Home **Home Activity:** Ask your child to show you how to write each letter.

**Handwriting** Letters *D, d*: Words with *d* **185**

Name _____

**Write**     **Color**

d          doll

d          dog

hammer

Dd

sun

d          duck

d          deer

**Directions:** Name each picture. Write *d* on the line if the word begins with /d/. Color the /d/ pictures.

**Home Activity:** Have your child find pictures that begin with /d/ and paste the pictures on paper to make a /d/ book.

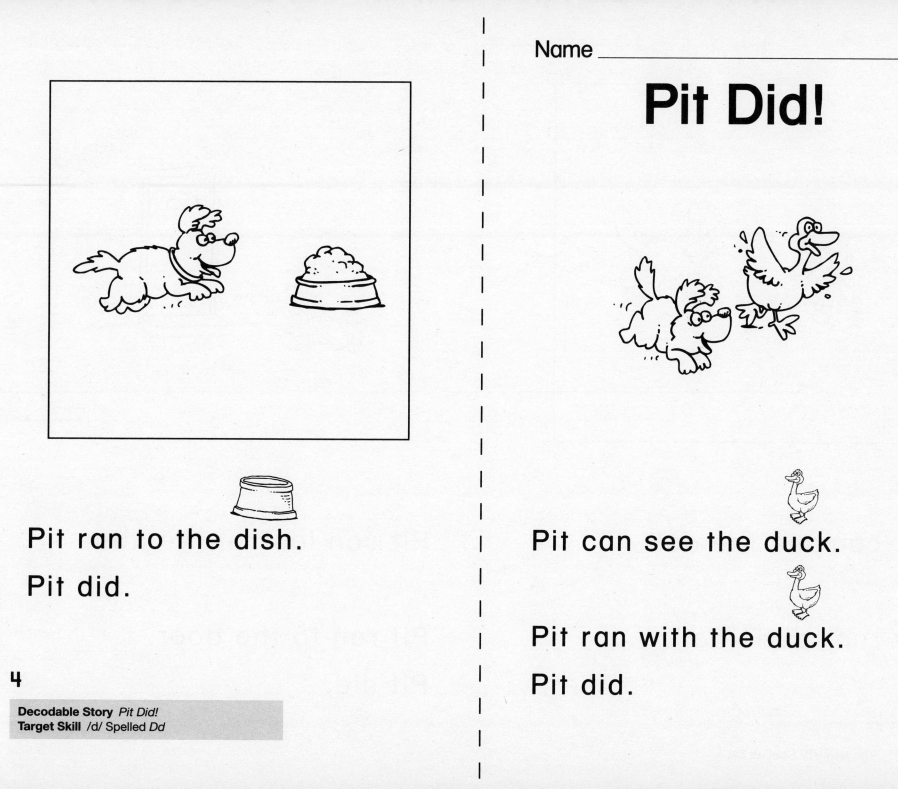

Pit ran to the dish.

Pit did.

4

**Decodable Story** *Pit Did!*
**Target Skill** /d/ Spelled *Dd*

# Pit Did!

Pit can see the duck.

Pit ran with the duck.

Pit did.

1

Pit can see the doll.

Pit ran to the doll.

Pit can look at the door.

Pit ran to the door.

Pit did.

Name _____

✏️ Write   🖍️ Color

see    look

_____

I can _____**see**_____ the cat.

🖍️

_____

_____**Look**_____ at me!

🖍️

_____

I _____**look**_____ for my cat.

🖍️

_____

Pat can _____**see**_____ the dog.

🖍️

© Pearson Education, Inc., K

🍎 **Directions:** Read each sentence. Write the missing word to finish the sentence. Color the picture..

**School + Home** **Home Activity:** Have your child use *see* and *look* in other sentences.

**High-Frequency Words   189**

Name _____

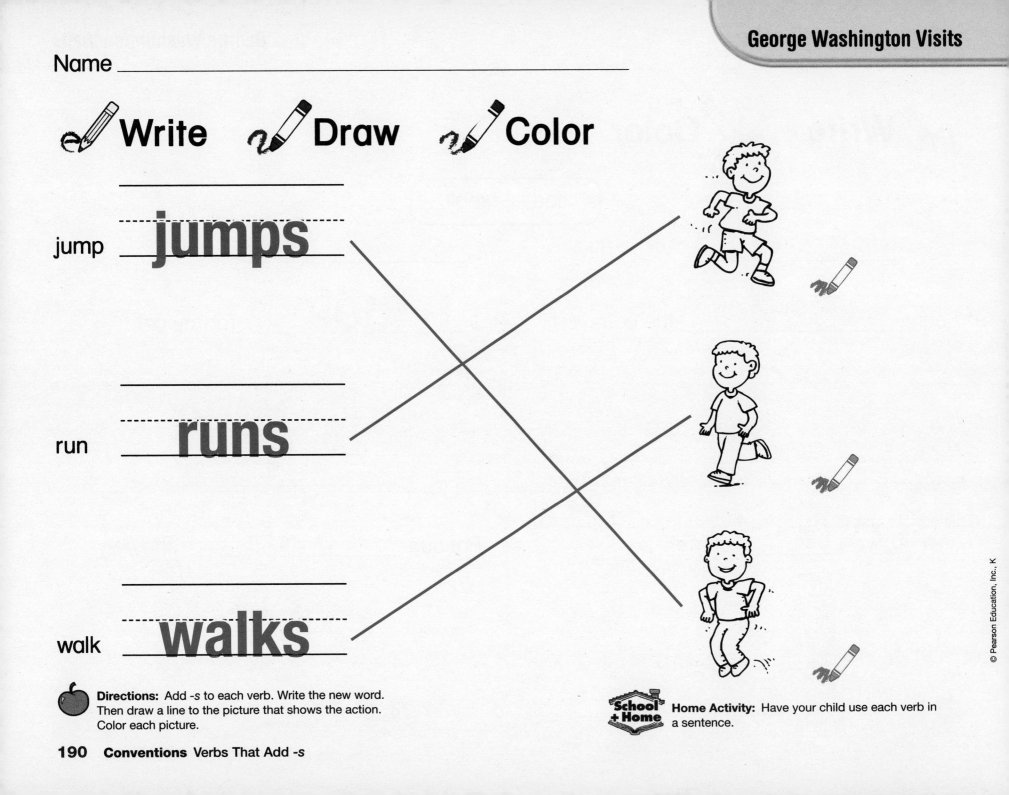

✏️ **Write**    🖍️ **Draw**    🖍️ **Color**

_____

jump    **jumps**

_____

run    **runs**

_____

walk    **walks**

**Directions:** Add -s to each verb. Write the new word. Then draw a line to the picture that shows the action. Color each picture.

**Home Activity:** Have your child use each verb in a sentence.

Name _____

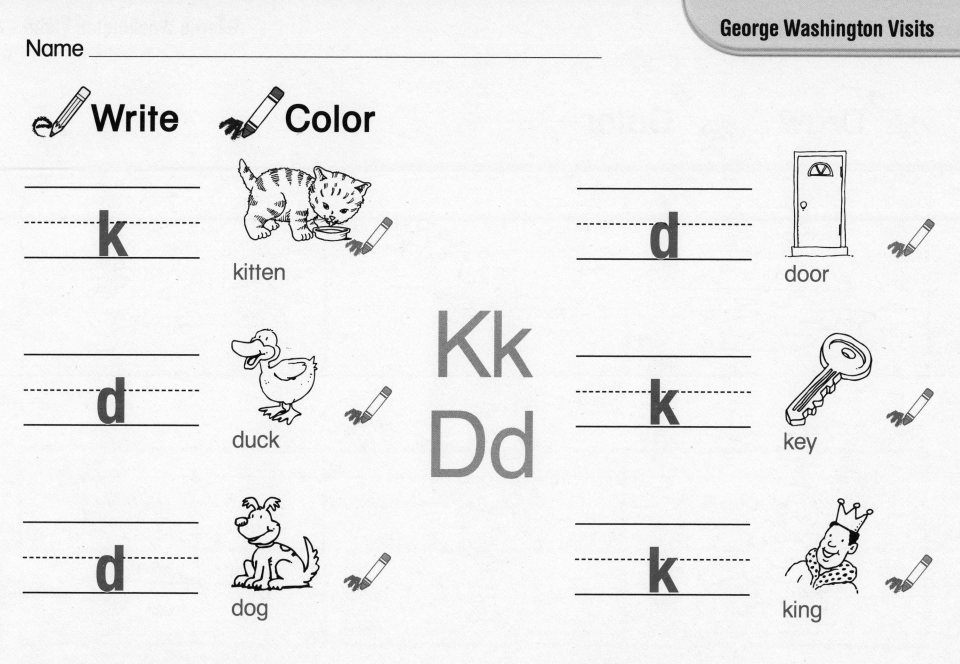

✏️ Write 🖍️ Color

| | | | |
|---|---|---|---|
| **k** | kitten | **d** | door |
| **d** | duck | **k** | key |
| **d** | dog | **k** | king |

**Kk Dd**

**Directions:** Name each picture. Write *k* on the line if the word begins with /k/ and *d* if it begins with /d/. Color the pictures.

**School + Home**

**Home Activity:** Have your child find other words that begin with /k/ or /d/.

**Phonics** /k/ Spelled *Kk* and /d/ Spelled *Dd*   **191**

Name _____

✏️ Draw   🖍️ Color

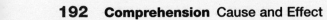

🍎 **Directions:** Draw a line from what happened to why it happened. Color each picture.

**School + Home** **Home Activity:** Have your child tell why each event happened.

Name _____

## Read It!

Tom packs.

Tom packed.

## Say It!

Say a sentence that tells something Tom does now. Then say a sentence that tells something Tom did yesterday.

## Write It!

walks
walked

- - - - - - - - - - - - - - - -
**walks**

looks
looked

- - - - - - - - - - - - - - - -
**looked**

**Directions** Have children read the sentences about Tom. Ask them to give sentences for things Tom does now and did yesterday. Then have children write the word that tells about each picture.

**School + Home**  **Home Activity** Have your child use the words in sentences.

Name _____

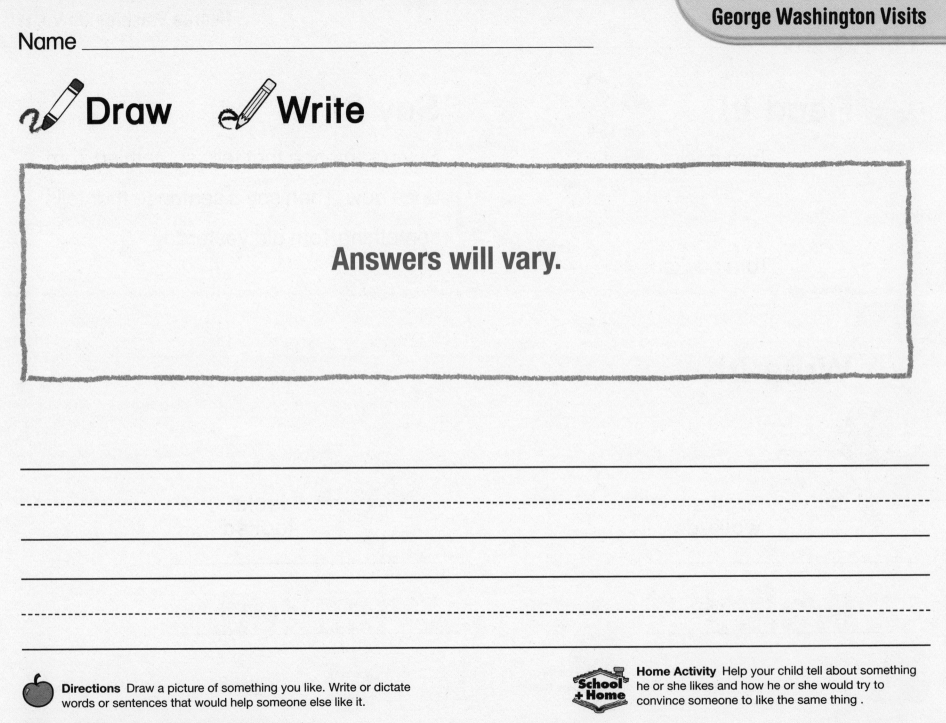

✎ Draw  ✎ Write

Answers will vary.

© Pearson Education, Inc., K

🍎 **Directions** Draw a picture of something you like. Write or dictate words or sentences that would help someone else like it.

**School + Home** **Home Activity** Help your child tell about something he or she likes and how he or she would try to convince someone to like the same thing .

Name _____

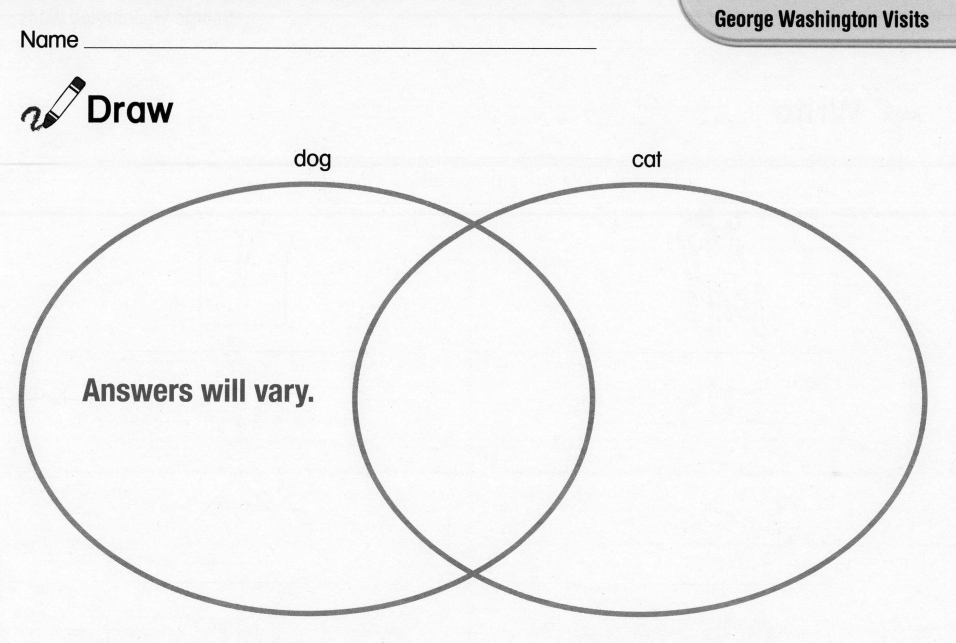

# ✏ Draw

dog           cat

**Answers will vary.**

**Directions:** In the left and right circles, draw pictures that show how a dog and a cat are different. In the space in the middle, draw a picture that shows how they are alike.

**Home Activity:** Have children explain the similarities and differences between two books.

**Comprehension** Compare and Contrast    **195**

Name _____

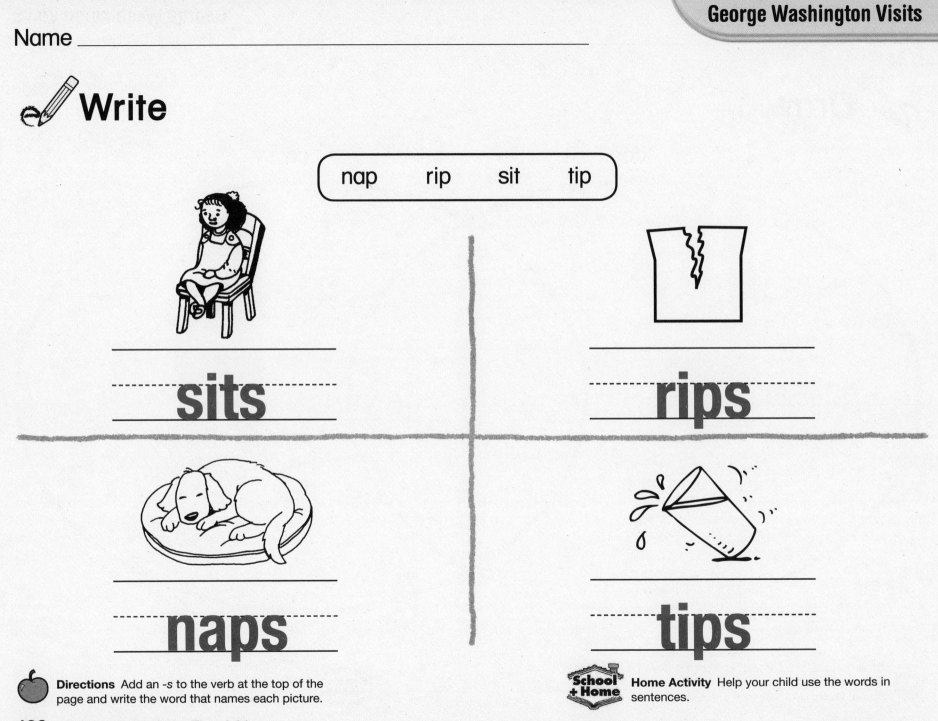

✏️ Write

nap    rip    sit    tip

**sits**

**rips**

**naps**

**tips**

**Directions** Add an *-s* to the verb at the top of the page and write the word that names each picture.

**School + Home**

**Home Activity** Help your child use the words in sentences.

Name _____

✏️ **Write**

F  F  F  F  F

f  f  f  f  f  f

**Fin** Fin

**fit** fit

🍎 **Directions:** Have children write a row of each letter and then write the words.

**Home Activity:** Ask your child to show you how to write each letter.

© Pearson Education, Inc., K

Name _____

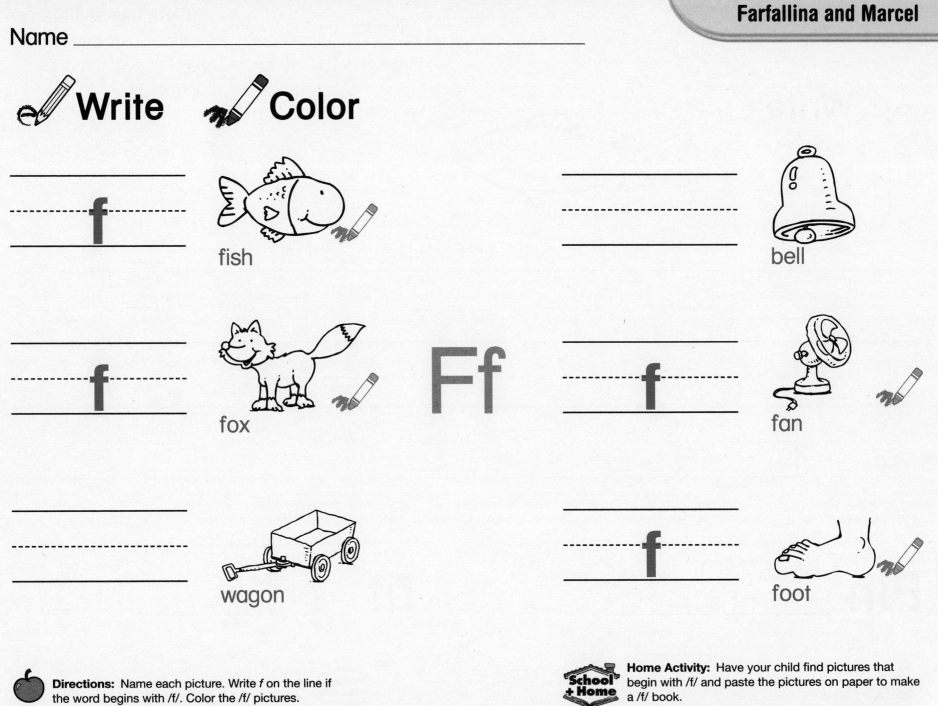

✏️ **Write**   🖍️ **Color**

f — fish

f — fox

— wagon

**Ff**

— bell

f — fan

f — foot

**Directions:** Name each picture. Write *f* on the line if the word begins with /f/. Color the /f/ pictures.

**Home Activity:** Have your child find pictures that begin with /f/ and paste the pictures on paper to make a /f/ book.

**School + Home**

I see a fin for me.

Look at the fin.

# For Me!

I see a fan for me.

Look at the fan.

I see a fox for me.

Look at the little fox.

2

I see a fish for me.

Look at the little fish.

3

Name _____

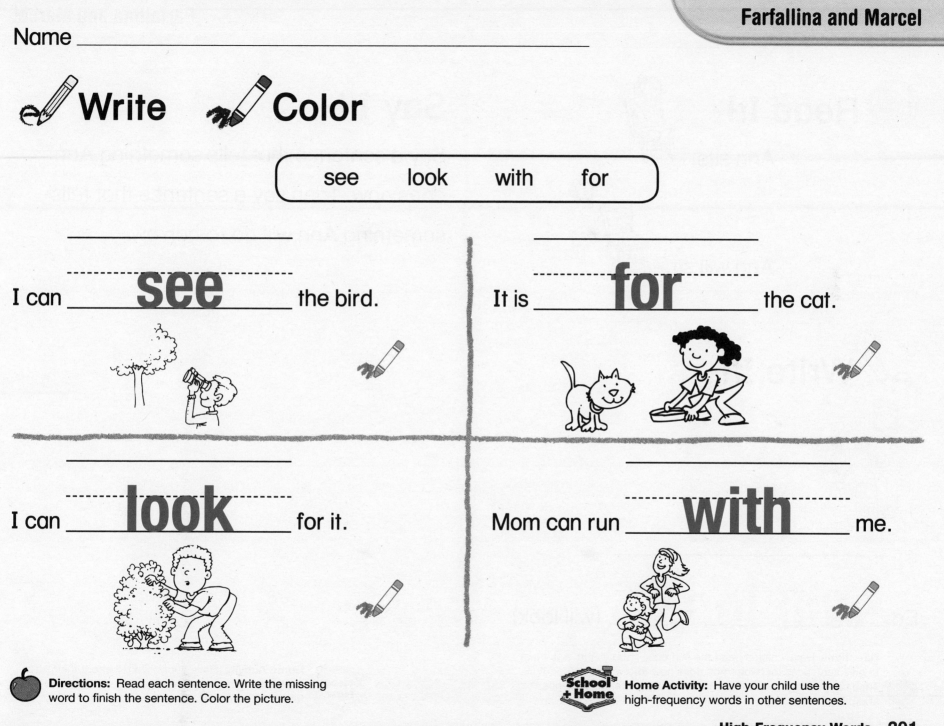

✏️ Write    🖍️ Color

| see | look | with | for |

_____

I can __**see**__ the bird.

_____

I can __**look**__ for it.

_____

It is __**for**__ the cat.

_____

Mom can run __**with**__ me.

🍎 **Directions:** Read each sentence. Write the missing word to finish the sentence. Color the picture.

**School + Home**

**Home Activity:** Have your child use the high-frequency words in other sentences.

Name _____

## Read It!

Ann sits.

Ann will sit.

## Say It!

Say a sentence that tells something Ann does now. Then say a sentence that tells something Ann will do tomorrow.

## Write It!

_____

Ed ___**will look**___. (will look)

**Directions** Have children read the sentences about Ann. Ask them to give sentences for things Ann does now and will do in the future. Then have children write the words that complete the sentence about Ed.

**Home Activity** Have your child tell about things that are happening now and things that will happen in the future.

Name _____

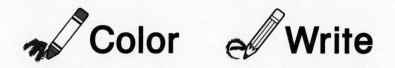 **Color**  **Write**

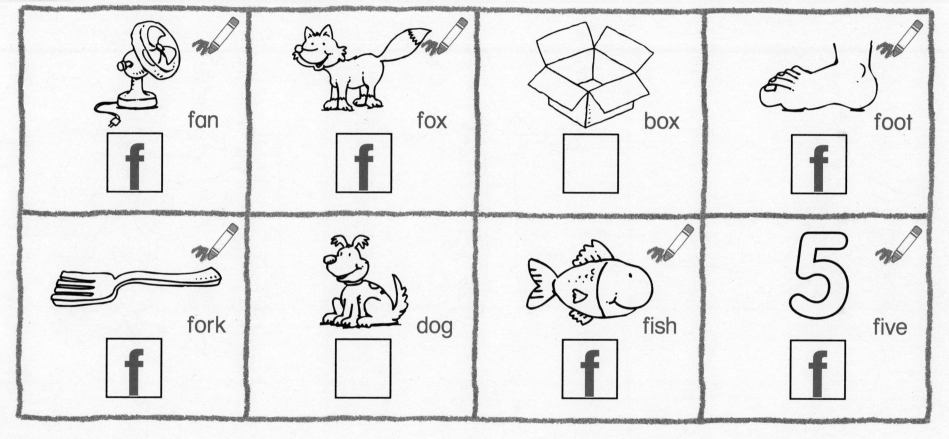

| | | | |
|---|---|---|---|
| fan | fox | box | foot |
| **f** | **f** | ☐ | **f** |
| fork | dog | fish | five |
| **f** | ☐ | **f** | **f** |

 **Directions:** Name the pictures. Color each picture that begins with /f/. Write *f* in the box.

 **Home Activity:** Have your child name the pictures that begin with /f/.

Name _____

 **Number**

| 3 | 2 | 1 |

 **Directions:** Number the pictures 1, 2, and 3 to tell the beginning, middle, and end of *Farfallina & Marcel*.

 **Home Activity:** Have your child tell what happens at the beginning, middle, and end of the story.

Name _____

✏️ Circle   ✏️ Write

hop   (hops)

_____

Pam _____ **hops** _____ to me.

sit   (sits)

_____

Tim _____ **sits** _____ in it.

pat   (pats)

_____

Nan _____ **pats** _____ the cat.

🍎 **Directions** Circle the word that completes the sentence. Write the word.

**School + Home** **Home Activity** Have your child create new sentences for the word choices.

Name _____

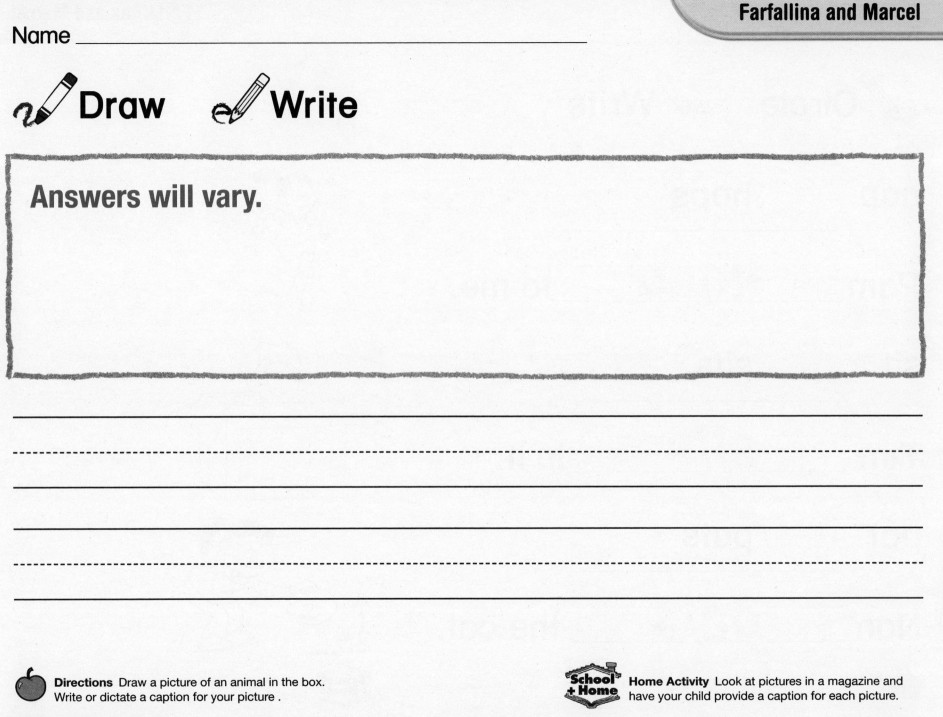

✏ Draw  ✏ Write

Answers will vary.

_____

- - - - - - - - - - - - - - - - - -

_____

- - - - - - - - - - - - - - - - - -

_____

- - - - - - - - - - - - - - - - - -

_____

**Directions** Draw a picture of an animal in the box.
Write or dictate a caption for your picture .

**School + Home** **Home Activity** Look at pictures in a magazine and
have your child provide a caption for each picture.

**206** **Writing** Captions

Name ___________________________________________

# Color

**Directions** Color the pictures of the two characters in the story.

**Home Activity** Have your child tell you about the two story characters, Farfallina and Marcel.

Name _____

### Read It!

Kim hops.

Kim will hop.

### Say It!

Say a sentence that tells something you are doing now. Then say a sentence that tells something you will do tomorrow.

### Write It!

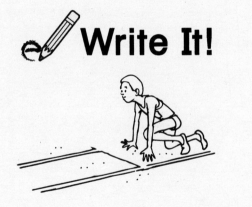

The man _____ **will run** _____. (will run)

**Directions** Have children read the sentences about Kim. Ask them to give sentences for things they do now and things they will do tomorrow. Then have children write the words that complete the sentence about the man.

**Home Activity** Have your child create sentences using the words on the page.

Name _____

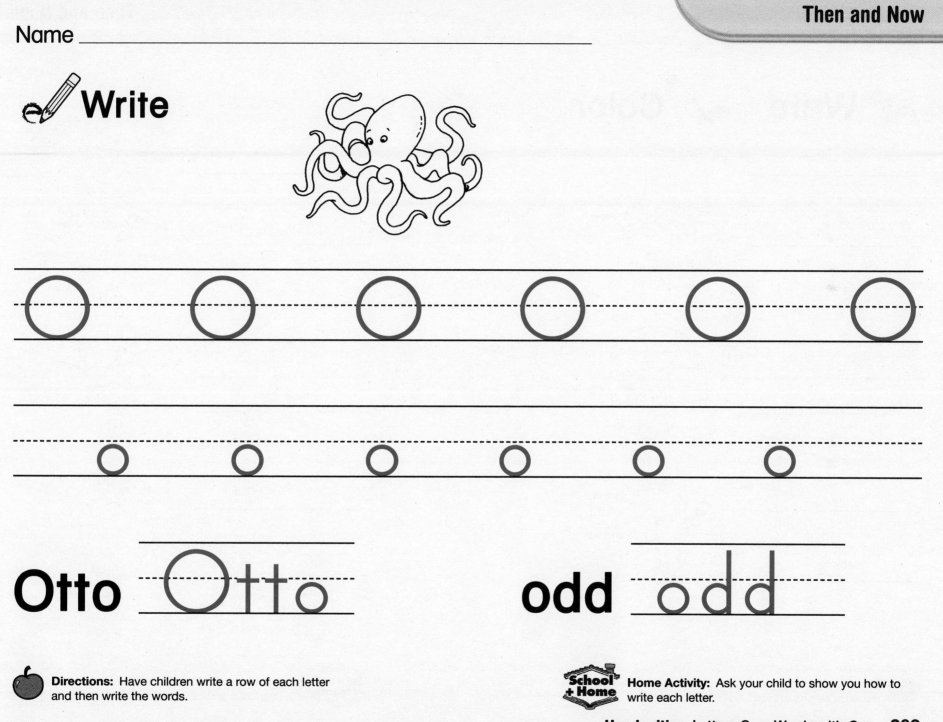

✏ **Write**

Otto ___Otto___

odd ___odd___

🍎 **Directions:** Have children write a row of each letter and then write the words.

🏫 **School + Home**

**Home Activity:** Ask your child to show you how to write each letter.

**Handwriting** Letters *O, o:* Words with *O, o* **209**

Name _____

✏️ **Write**    🖍️ **Color**

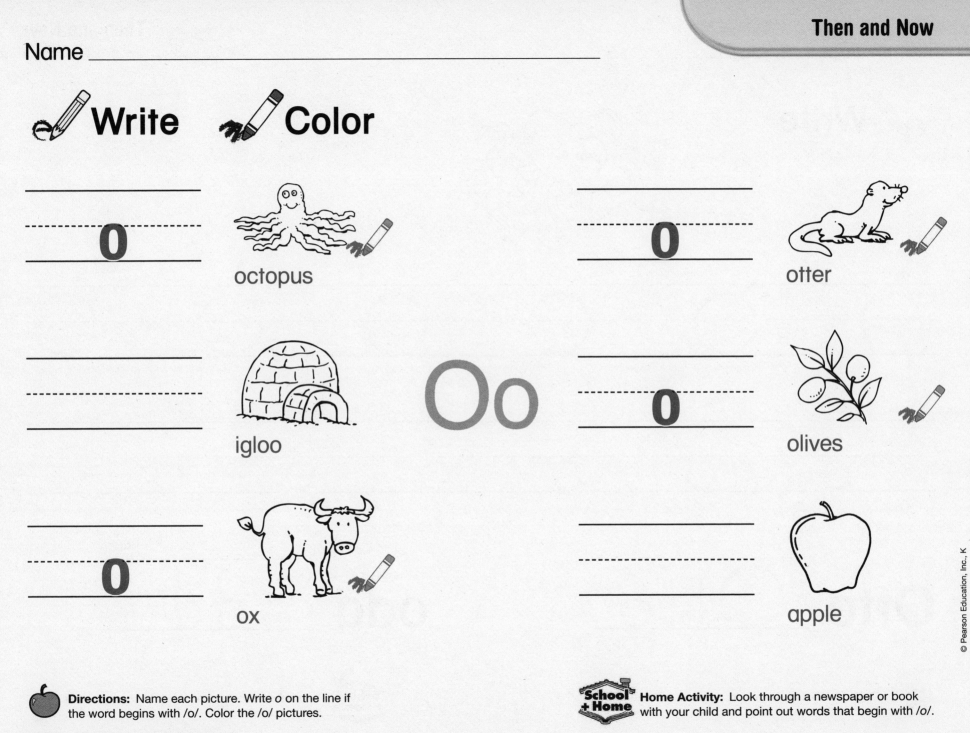

_____
**O** - - - - - - - - - - - - - - - -
_____
octopus

_____
- - - - - - - - - - - - - - - -
_____
igloo

_____
**O** - - - - - - - - - - - - - - - -
_____
ox

**Oo**

_____
**O** - - - - - - - - - - - - - - - -
_____
otter

_____
**O** - - - - - - - - - - - - - - - -
_____
olives

_____
- - - - - - - - - - - - - - - -
_____
apple

🍎 **Directions:** Name each picture. Write *o* on the line if the word begins with /o/. Color the /o/ pictures.

**School + Home** **Home Activity:** Look through a newspaper or book with your child and point out words that begin with /o/.

Little Rob is not sad.

Little Rob can have
the top.

**Decodable Story** *Little Rob*
**Target Skill** /o/ Spelled *Oo*

# Little Rob

Little Rob is sad.

He is little.

Little Rob is on a mat.

He is sad.

Little Rob can see a top.

Can he have the top?

Name _____

Write  Color

they    of    you    she

Can _____ **she** _____ see you?

It is a lot _____ **of** _____ fun.

Can _____ **you** _____ see the top?

_____ **They** _____ can see the fox.

**Directions:** Read each sentence. Write the missing word to finish the sentence. Color the picture.

**Home Activity:** Have your child use the high-frequency words in other sentences.

Name _____

# Read ✏️ Draw

**Answers will vary.**

We have a bat.

Rob can mop.

It is a fan.

🍎 **Directions:** Read each sentence. Draw a picture that shows the meaning of word group.

**School + Home** **Home Activity:** Have your child read the meaningful word groups and tell about his or her pictures.

**214** **Conventions** Meaningful Word Groups

Name _____

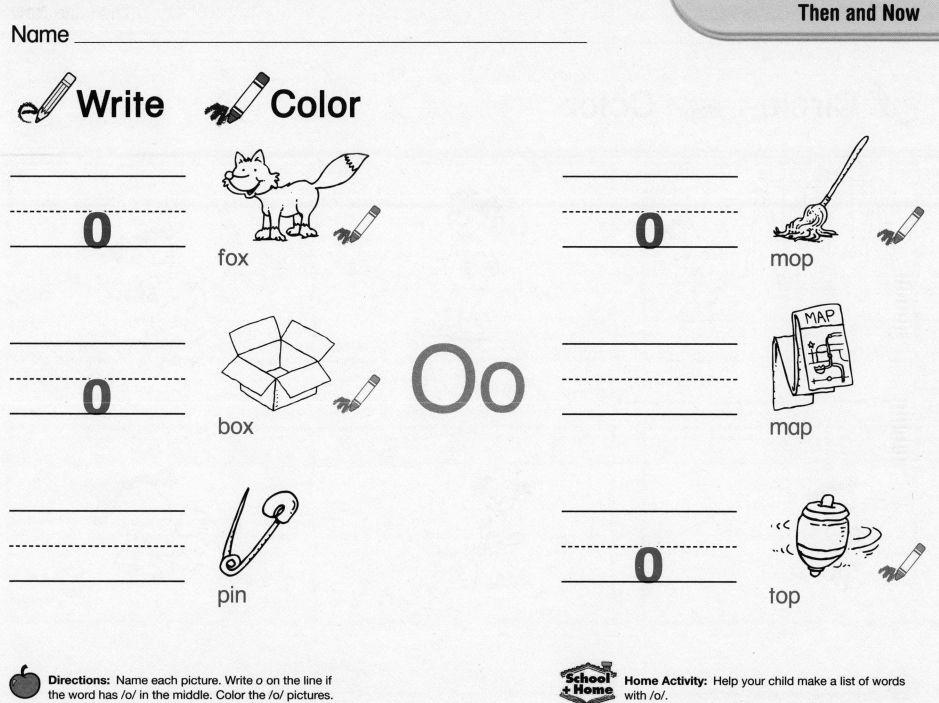

**Write**   **Color**

O                fox

O                mop

O                box

Oo               map

                 pin

O                top

**Directions:** Name each picture. Write *o* on the line if the word has /o/ in the middle. Color the /o/ pictures.

**School + Home**  **Home Activity:** Help your child make a list of words with /o/.

Name _____

 Circle    Color

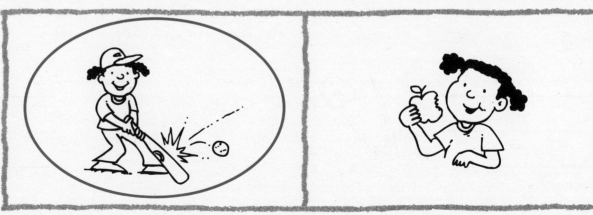

 **Directions:** Circle the picture that shows what you think the child would do next. Color the picture

 **Home Activity:** Have your child explain how he or she arrived at his or her conclusion.

**216**   **Comprehension** Draw Conclusions

Name _____

## Read It!

Dan will see the bird.

Dan sees the bird.

## Say It!

Say a sentence that tells something you can see now. Then say a sentence that tells something you might see tomorrow.

## Write It!

The girl _____ **will eat** _____ the apple. (will eat)

 **Directions** Have children read the sentences about Dan. Ask them to give sentences for things they see now and things they will see tomorrow. Then have children write the words that complete the sentence about the girl.

 **Home Activity** Have your child use the action words in sentences.

Name _____

## ✏️ Write

1. Answers will vary.

2.

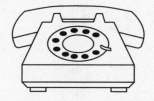

3.

**Directions** After listening to class discussions about now and the past, take notes by writing or dictating a list of things from the past that you want to learn more about.

 **Home Activity** Help your child write a list of things to do on a rainy day.

Name _____

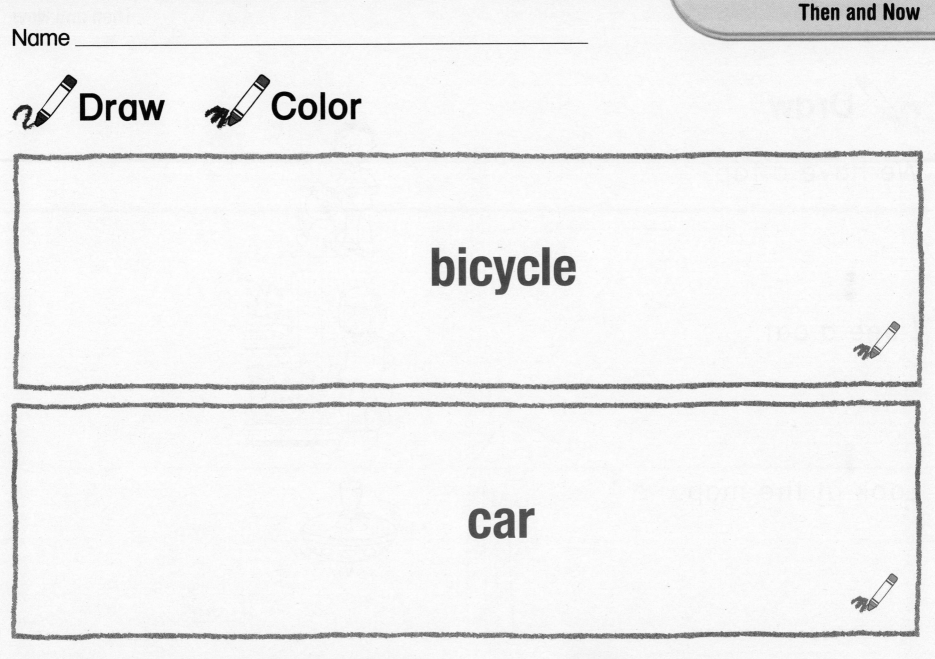

✏️ **Draw**   🖍️ **Color**

bicycle

car

**Directions:** Compare and contrast a bicycle and a car. Draw the slower thing in the top box and color it. Draw the faster thing in the bottom box and color it. Tell how the two things are alike and different.

**School + Home**

**Home Activity:** Ask children how a bicycle and a car are alike and different.

Name _____

## ✏️ Draw

We have a top.

I see a cat.

Look at the map.

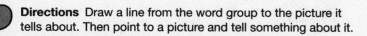
**Directions** Draw a line from the word group to the picture it tells about. Then point to a picture and tell something about it.

**Home Activity** Point to things around the house and have your child create a meaningful word group about each item.

**220** **Conventions** Meaningful Word Groups

Name _____

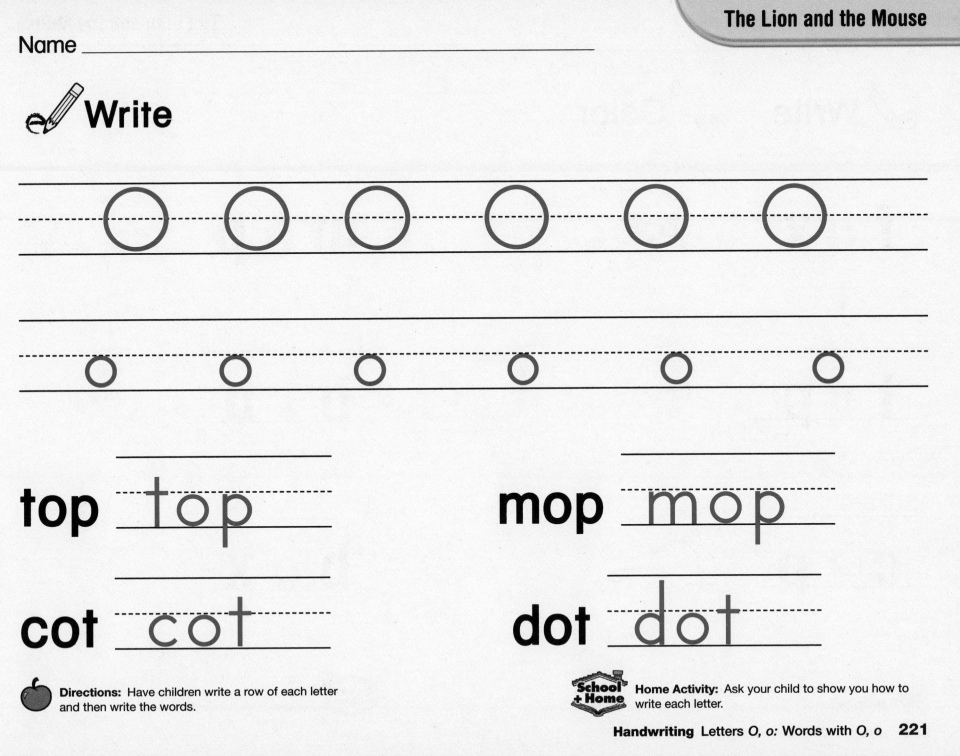

✏️ **Write**

top _top_

cot _cot_

mop _mop_

dot _dot_

**Directions:** Have children write a row of each letter and then write the words.

**Home Activity:** Ask your child to show you how to write each letter.

**Handwriting** Letters O, o: Words with O, o   **221**

Name _____

✏️ Write ✏️ Color

f o x

t o p

**Oo**

c a p

m o p

b i b

b o x

🍎 **Directions:** Write *o*, *a*, or *i* to finish each word. Color the /o/ pictures.

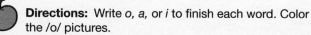

**Home Activity:** Have your child write *mop* and *map* and draw a picture for each word.

It is not on the rat.

It is in the pot.

4

**Decodable Story** *A Cap for Tom*
**Target Skill** /o/ Spelled *Oo*

# A Cap for Tom

Tom can have a cap.

Is the cap on Tom?

1

The cap is not on Tom.
See the cap.

The cap is not on Tom.
It is on the rat.

Name _____

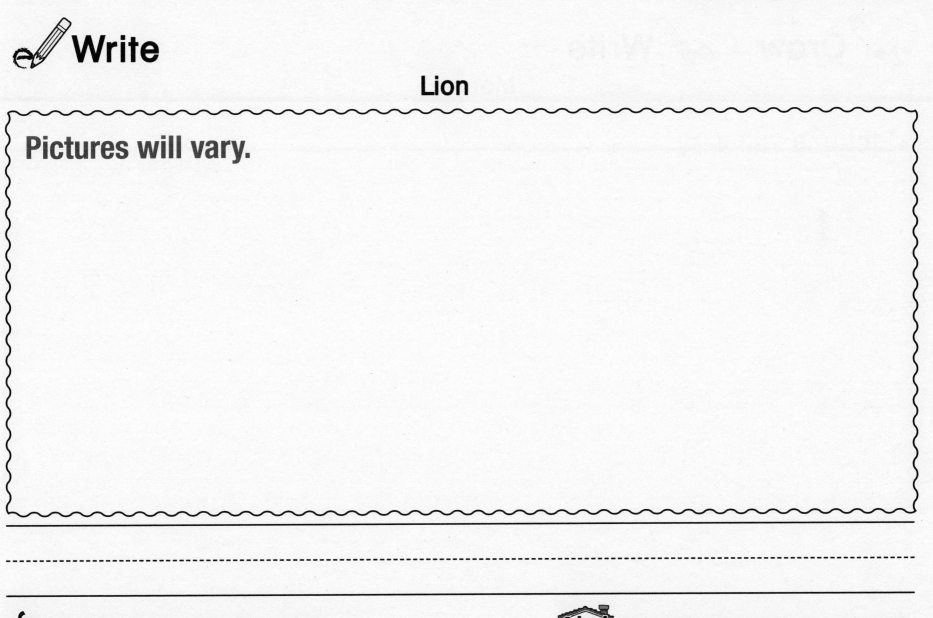

## ✏️ Write

### Lion

Pictures will vary.

 **Directions:** Have children draw a picture of a lion and then write an idea from the class chart.

 **Home Activity:** Ask your child to tell you about the picture.

Name _____

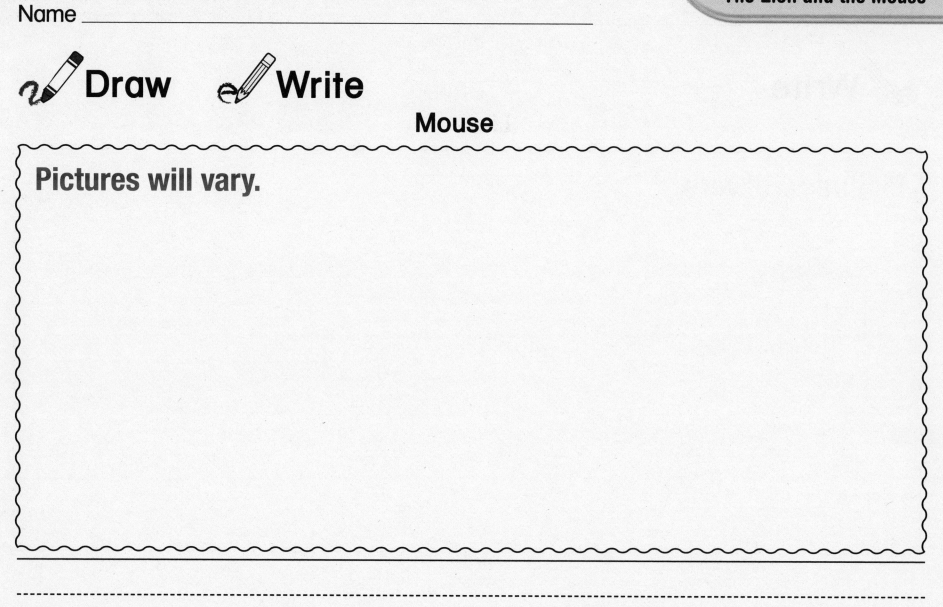

✏️ Draw   ✏️ Write

**Mouse**

Pictures will vary.

**Directions:** Have children draw a picture of a mouse and then write an idea from the class chart.

**School + Home**   **Home Activity:** Ask your child to explain the class's ideas for a poem.

Name _____

✏️ **Write**   🖍️ **Color**

| they | of | you | we |

_____

**We** _____ can see the dog.

_____

I see a lot _____ **of** _____ dogs.

_____

They can run to _____ **you** _____.

_____

_____ **They** _____ ran to me.

**Directions:** Read each sentence . Write the missing word to finish the sentence. Color the picture.

**School + Home**

**Home Activity:** Have your child use the high-frequency words in other sentences.

Name _____

 **Draw**

Ron can see the rod.

Mop pin is my.

Mom is at the top.

**Directions:** Read each group of words. If the words make a sentence, draw a picture that shows the meaning of the sentence.

 **Home Activity:** Have your child read each group of words and tell which words do not make a sentence.

Name _____

Draw

| Beginning | Middle | End |
|---|---|---|
| Pictures will vary. | | |

 **Directions:** Have children draw pictures of the events for the beginning, middle, and end of the class poem.

 **Home Activity:** Have your child tell you the sequence of events in the class poem.

Name _____

 Write

## Beginning

Answers will vary.

_____
- - - - - - - - - - - - - - - - - - - - - - - - - - - - - - - - - - - - - - - -
_____

## Middle

_____
- - - - - - - - - - - - - - - - - - - - - - - - - - - - - - - - - - - - - - - -
_____

## End

_____
- - - - - - - - - - - - - - - - - - - - - - - - - - - - - - - - - - - - - - - -
_____

 **Directions** Have children write or dictate words and sentences about the events for the beginning, middle, and end of the class poem.

 **School + Home** **Home Activity** Ask your child to read the words or sentences to you..

Name _____

# Circle   # Color

| | | | |
|---|---|---|---|
| fix<br>(fox) |  | (map)<br>mop | |
| (cab)<br>cob | | tap<br>(top) | |

**Directions:** Circle the word that names the picture.
Color the /o/ pictures.

**School + Home**  **Home Activity:** Have your child draw a picture of an /o/ word.

**Phonics** /o/ Spelled *Oo*   **231**

Name _____

✏️ **Color**

**Directions:** Color the picture that shows the main idea of the story *The Lion and the Mouse*.

**School + Home** **Home Activity:** Have your child tell what lesson the lion learned from the mouse.

Name _____

 **Circle**

Pam got a cap.

(Pam got a top.)

Tom had a map.

Tom had a mat.

Nan sat.

(Nan ran.)

Tim ran to Tom.

Tim ran to Pam.

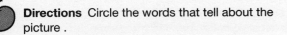 **Directions** Circle the words that tell about the picture.

 **Home Activity** Have your child read the word groups to you and tell about the pictures.

**Conventions** Meaningful Word Groups **233**

Name _____

✏️ Draw    ✏️ Write

## Details to Add

| | | |
|---|---|---|
| Pictures and answers will vary. | | |

_____

- - - - - - - - - - - - - - - - - - - - - - - - - - - -

_____

- - - - - - - - - - - - - - - - - - - - - - - - - - - -

_____

- - - - - - - - - - - - - - - - - - - - - - - - - - - -

_____

🍎 **Directions** Have children draw pictures or write words or sentences with details about the class poem.

**School + Home**

**Home Activity** Ask your child to explain how the details can be added to the class poem.

Name _____

 **Number** **Color**

 **Directions:** Number the pictures in each row to tell what happened first, next, and last. Color the pictures.

 **Home Activity:** Help your child tell about things he or she did, noting what happened in order.

**Comprehension** Plot  **235**

Name _____

✏️ **Circle**

(Pam can pat the cat.)

Pam the cat can.

mat Sam on sat.

(Sam sat on the mat.)

A little got Nan.

(Nan got a little cap.)

(The man sat.)

Sat man the.

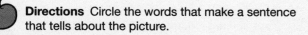
**Directions** Circle the words that make a sentence that tells about the picture.

**Home Activity** Ask your child to create another sentence for each picture.

Name _____

✏️ Circle   ✏️ Write

1. the mouse is scared.

_____

- - - - - - - - - - - - - - - - - - - - - - -

_____

2. he is now a big lion.

_____

- - - - - - - - - - - - - - - - - - - - - - -

_____

3. they will be friends.

_____

- - - - - - - - - - - - - - - - - - - - - - -

_____

**Directions** Have children circle the mistakes and rewrite the words or sentences correctly on the lines.

**Home Activity** Ask your child to explain how he or she fixed the mistakes in the sentences.

Name _____

✏️ # Write

Answers will vary.

---

**Directions** Have children copy sentences from the class poem using correct spacing between letters and words and correct capitalization.

 **Home Activity** Help your child edit the sentences by checking for correct letter and word spacing and capitalization.

Name _____

✏ Draw    ✏ Write

**Pictures and answers will vary.**

_____

Title: _____

_____

Author: _____

**Directions** Have children draw a picture for a cover for their poem. Help them write the poem's title and their name.

**School + Home**  **Home Activity** Have your child explain how the picture and title go with the poem.

Name _____

✏️ Circle   ✏️ Write

I shared my poem with _____ **Answers will vary.** _____.

Here's what he/she thought about my poem.

_____

_____

_____

_____

_____

© Pearson Education, Inc., K

**Directions** Have children circle the picture that shows with whom they shared their poem. Then have children ask the peer or adult reviewer to fill in the blanks and to discuss the poem with him or her.

**School + Home** **Home Activity** Ask your child to read or tell the class poem to you.

Name _____

 **Write**

H          H          H          H          H          H

h          h          h          h          h          h

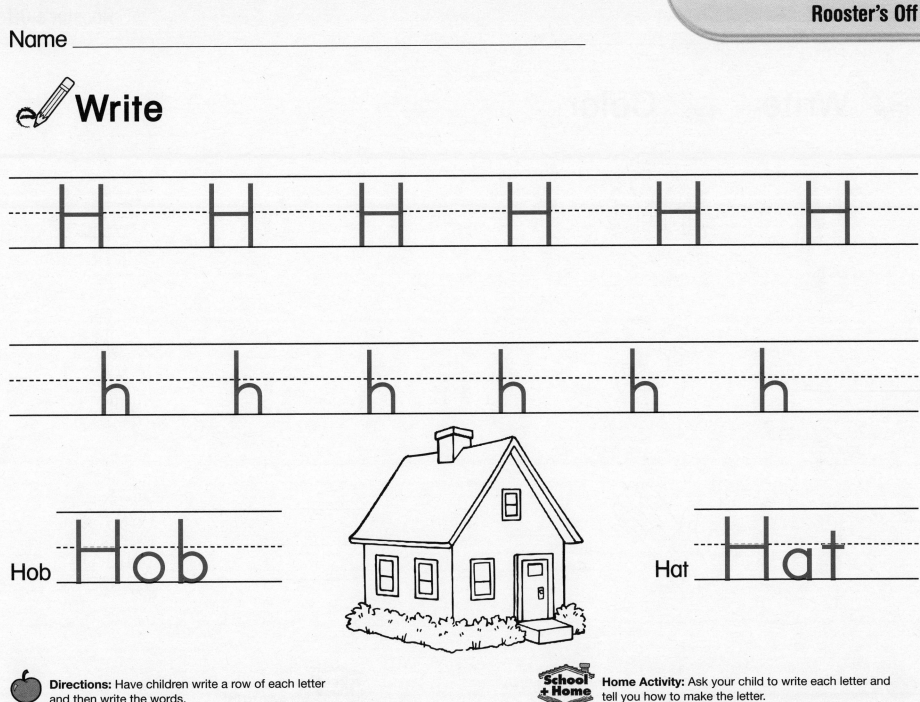

Hob  Hob

Hat  Hat

**Directions:** Have children write a row of each letter and then write the words.

**School + Home**

**Home Activity:** Ask your child to write each letter and tell you how to make the letter.

**Handwriting** Letters *H, h*: Words with *h*  **241**

Name _____

✎ Write    🖍 Color

h    house

duck

h    hand

**Hh**

h    helicopter

h    horse

lion

**Directions:** Name the pictures. Write *h* on the line if the word begins with /h/. Color the /h/ pictures.

**Home Activity:** Have your child find other words with /h/ such as *hat*.

I like my hat.

Do you like my hat?

4

Name _____

# I Have!

I have a hat.

The hat is little.

That is my hat.

1

The hat is on me.

It is my little hat.

Do you have a little hat?

2

I can hop with the hat.

I can hit with the hat.

3

Name _____

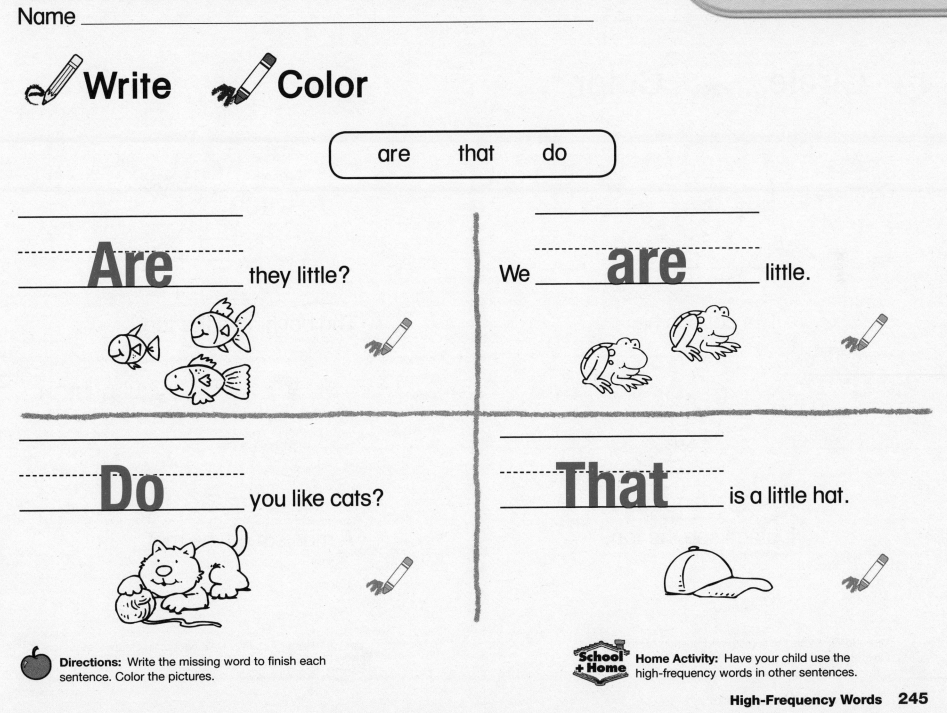

✏️ **Write**   🖍️ **Color**

| are | that | do |

_____

**Are** _____ they little?

We _____ **are** little.

**Do** _____ you like cats?

**That** _____ is a little hat.

**Directions:** Write the missing word to finish each sentence. Color the pictures.

**School + Home** **Home Activity:** Have your child use the high-frequency words in other sentences.

© Pearson Education, Inc., K

Name _____

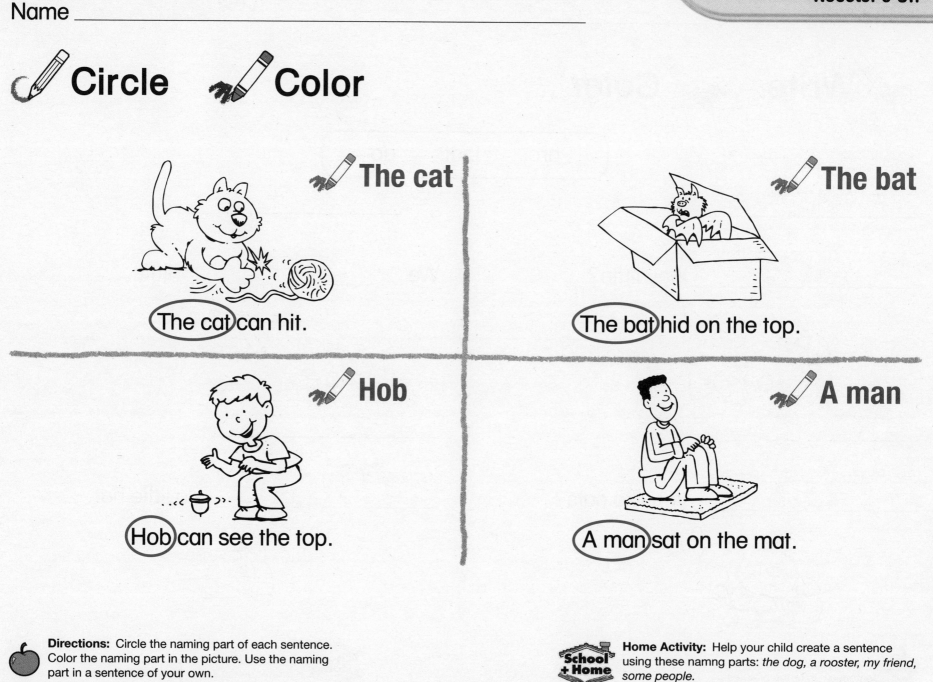

🖊 **Circle**   🖍 **Color**

🖍 **The cat**

The cat can hit.

🖍 **The bat**

The bat hid on the top.

🖍 **Hob**

Hob can see the top.

🖍 **A man**

A man sat on the mat.

🍎 **Directions:** Circle the naming part of each sentence. Color the naming part in the picture. Use the naming part in a sentence of your own.

🏫 **School + Home**  **Home Activity:** Help your child create a sentence using these namng parts: *the dog, a rooster, my friend, some people.*

Name _____

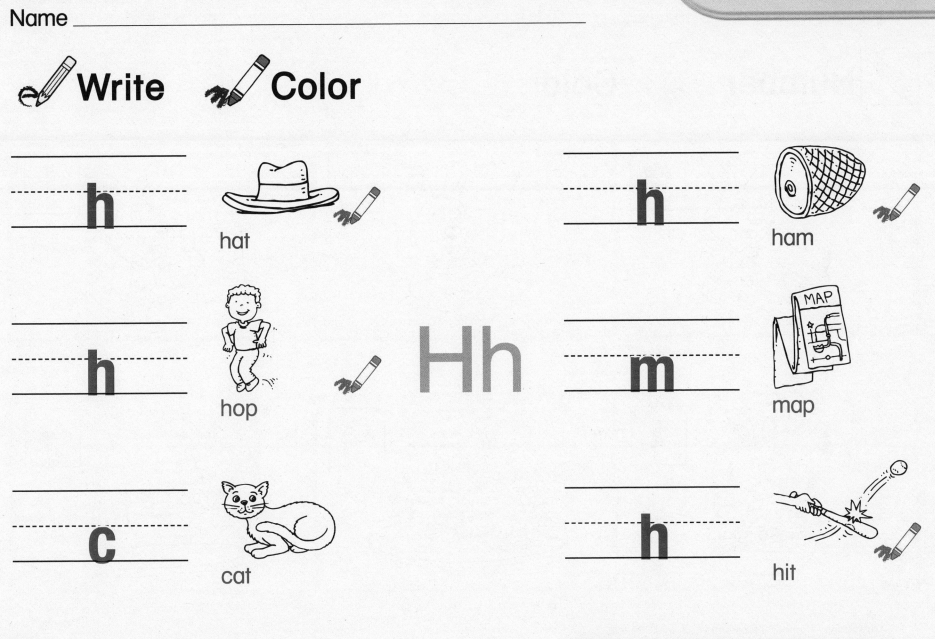

✏️ Write   🖍️ Color

h
hat

h
hop

c
cat

Hh

h
ham

m
map

h
hit

© Pearson Education, Inc., K

**Directions:** Name each picture. Write the letter for the beginning sound. Color the /h/ pictures.

**Home Activity:** Have your child write rhyming /h/ words for the words *cat*, *top*, and *sit* and then draw a picture for each word.

Name _____

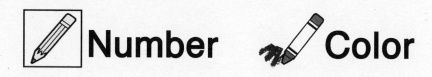
Number    Color

**Directions:** Number the pictures 1, 2, and 3 to tell what happened first, next, and last. Have children retell the sequence using the words *first, next,* and *last.* Then have them color the pictures.

**School + Home**  **Home Activity:** Have your child tell the steps to draw a picture.

Name _____

 **Circle**

Hat have little.

(I have a hat.)

(Hob can hit it.)

It can Hob.

The on the hat.

(The cat sat on the hat.)

(That hat is little.)

Little is hat.

**Directions:** Circle the words that make a sentence that tell about the picture. Help children tell why the words they chose make a complete sentence.

 **Home Activity:** Ask your child to create another sentence for each picture.

Name _____

✏️ **Write**

| Walk | Turn | Stop |

_____ _____ _____

**Walk**  **Turn**  **Stop**

🍎 **Directions** Give directions to go to the mailbox. Write the word for each picture.

🏠 **School + Home** **Home Activity** Help your child read the words to give directions for mailing a letter.

Name _____

 Color

 **Directions:** Color the pictures that are alike in each row. Tell how the pictures are alike.

 **Home Activity:** Have your child tell how the pictures are alike and how they are different.

**Comprehension** Compare and Contrast **251**

Name _____

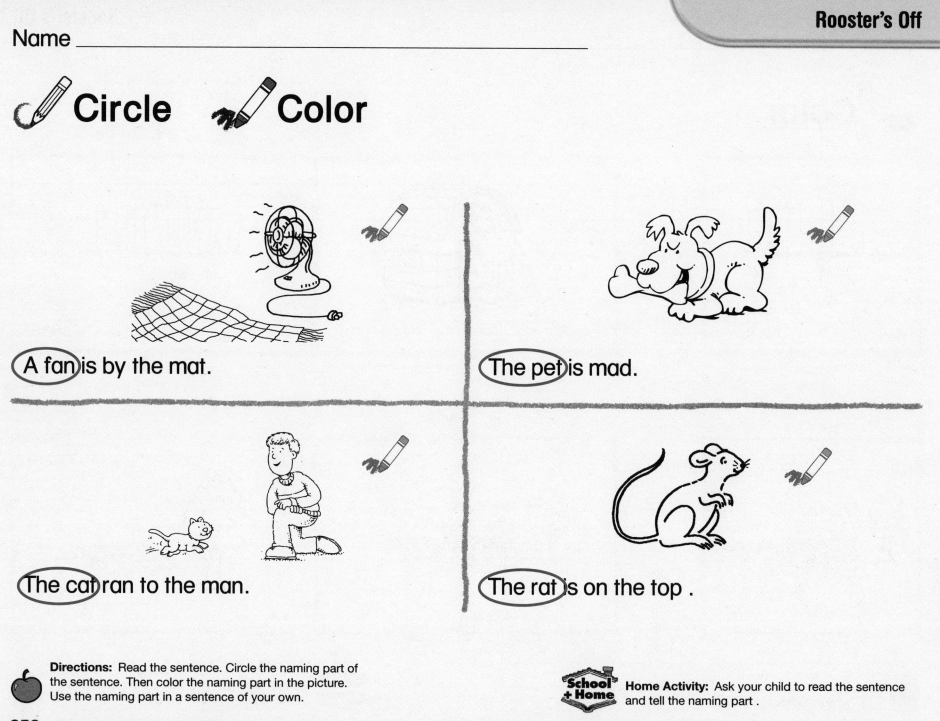

✏️ Circle    🖍️ Color

A fan is by the mat.

The pet is mad.

The cat ran to the man.

The rat is on the top .

**Directions:** Read the sentence. Circle the naming part of the sentence. Then color the naming part in the picture. Use the naming part in a sentence of your own.

**School + Home** **Home Activity:** Ask your child to read the sentence and tell the naming part .

Name _____

✏️ Write

L L L L L L

I I I I I I

Lad **Lad**

lid **lid**

🍎 **Directions:** Have children write a row of each letter and then write the words.

🏠 **School + Home** **Home Activity:** Ask your child to show you how to write each letter.

Name _____

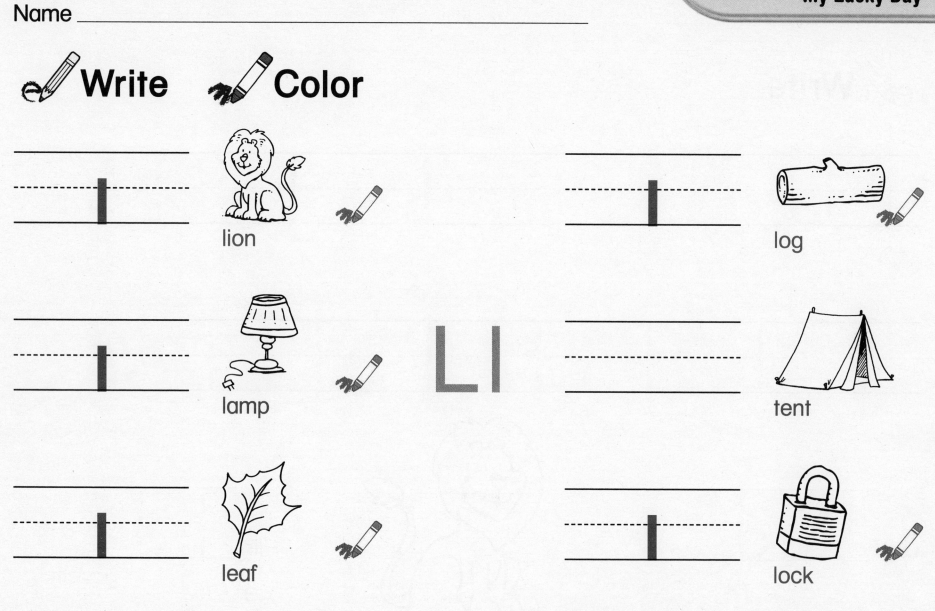

✏️ Write    🖍️ Color

lion

lamp

leaf

L l

log

tent

lock

**Directions:** Name each picture. Write *l* on the line if the word begins with /l/. Color the /l/ pictures.

**Home Activity:** Have your child find pictures that begin with /l/ and paste the pictures on paper to make a /l/ book.

**254 Phonics** /l/ Spelled *Ll*

# Lad and Me

Lad is my cat.

Lad is little.

Do you like Lad?

Lad can hop on the lid.

I can do that.

Are we on the lid?

**Decodable Story** *Lad and Me*
**Target Skill** /l/ Spelled *Ll*

I like Lad.

Lad can sit in my lap.

Lad can sit a lot.

Lad can hop.

Lad can hop a lot.

I can do that.

Name _____

✏️ **Write**  🖍️ **Color**

[ do     that     are ]

_____

**Do** _____ you see the man?

_____

Is _____ **that** _____ the lid?

_____

We _____ **are** _____ at the top.

_____

_____ **Do** _____ you like my cat?

🍎 **Directions:** Read each sentence. Write the missing word to finish the sentence. Color the picture.

🏫 School + Home  **Home Activity:** Have your child use the high-frequency words in other sentences.

© Pearson Education, Inc., K

Name _____

✏️ **Circle**    🖍️ **Color**

The cat (ran).

The lad (hops).

The rat (hid).

Nan (taps).

**Directions:** Circle the action part of the sentence and color the picture that shows the action. Use the action part in a sentence of your own.

**School + Home**  **Home Activity:** Help your child write simple sentences and identify the action part in each sentence.

**258**  **Conventions** Action Parts

© Pearson Education, Inc., K

Name _____

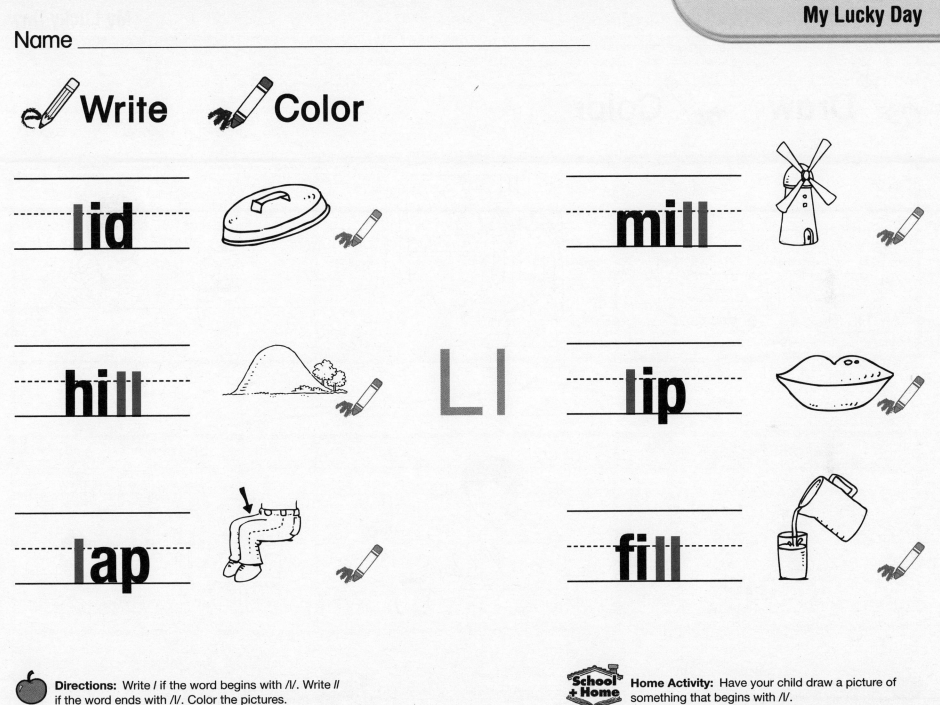

✏️ Write    🖍️ Color

lid

hill

lap

L l

mill

lip

fill

🍎 **Directions:** Write *l* if the word begins with /l/. Write *ll* if the word ends with /l/. Color the pictures.

**School + Home** **Home Activity:** Have your child draw a picture of something that begins with /l/.

**Phonics** /l/ Spelled *Ll*    **259**

Name _____

✏️ Draw   🖍️ Color

**Directions:** Draw a line from what happened to why it happened. Color each picture.

**Home Activity:** Have your child tell why each event happened.

Name _____

 Circle 🖍 Color

A cat ran fast.

Nan sits on it.

Tim hits the lid.

Lad can hop.

**Directions:** Circle the naming part of the sentence. Then color the naming part of the picture. Then use the naming part in a sentence of your own.

 **Home Activity:** Have your child read each sentence and tell the naming part.

Name _____

✏️ Write  🖍️ Draw

_____

- - - - - - - - - - - - - - - - - - - - - - - - - - - - - - - -

_____

- - - - - - - - - - - - - - - - - - - - - - - - - - - - - - - -

_____

_____

**Answers will vary.**

**Directions** Have children copy the class poem they wrote about the fox. Then have them draw a picture of the fox.

**School + Home** **Home Activity** Help your child make a poem with rhyming words such as *hit, bit, fit, kit,* and *sit.*

Name _____

## ✎ Draw

| | |
|---|---|
| | **Pictures will vary.** |

| | |
|---|---|
| | **Pictures will vary.** |

**Directions:** Draw a picture to show what happens next.

School + Home

**Home Activity:** Ask your child to tell the beginning of the story and then tell about what happens next.

Name _____

✏ **Circle**    ✏ **Write**

runs
(sits)

The dog **sits** .

pets
(hops)

The frog **hops** .

(mop)
hit

I **mop** .

mops
(pats)

She **pats** the cat.

hit
sit

I **hit** it.

sits
(taps)

He **taps** it.

🍎 **Directions:** Circle the action word to finish the sentence. Write the word on the lines.

**School + Home**

**Home Activity:** Have children read each sentence.

**264** **Conventions** Action Parts

Name _____

✏️ **Write**

1   one

1 one

2   two

2 two

3   three

3 three

4   four

4 four

5   five

5 five

🍎 **Directions:** Write each number and number word on the lines.

**Home Activity:** Ask your child to draw pictures to show each number.

**Handwriting** Numerals and Number Words   **265**

Name _____

✏️ **Write**  🖍️ **Color**

pl — plant

sl — sled

fl — flag

cl — clap

pl — plug

sl — slide

**Directions:** Name each picture. Write the blend for the beginning sound. Color the pictures.

**Home Activity:** Have your child point out initial consonant blends in the words in a book or magazine.

I can tap.

Tap is like trap.

Do you see one trap?

**Decodable Story** *My Words*
**Target Skill** Consonant Blends

# My Words

I have one cap.

Cap is like clap.

Can you clap?

I see one cab.

Cab is like crab.

Can you see three?

I can see one pot.

Pot is like spot.

Do you see two?

Name _____

✏️ **Write**   🖍️ **Color**

| one   two   three   four   five |

_____

I see ____ **four** ____ flags.

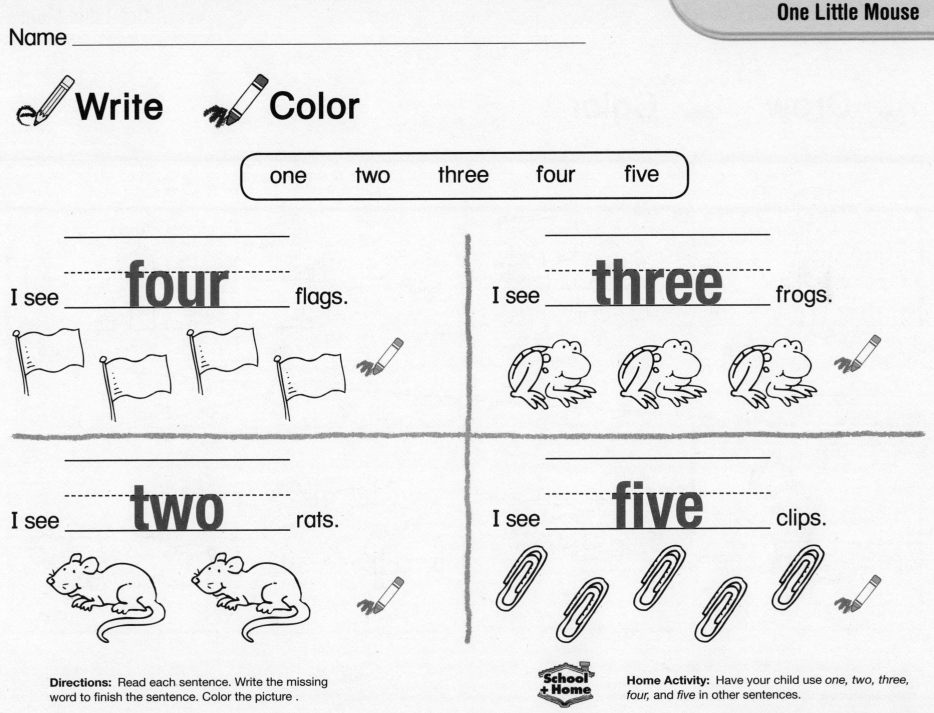

_____

I see ____ **three** ____ frogs.

_____

I see ____ **two** ____ rats.

_____

I see ____ **five** ____ clips.

**Directions:** Read each sentence. Write the missing word to finish the sentence. Color the picture .

**School + Home**

**Home Activity:** Have your child use *one, two, three, four,* and *five* in other sentences.

Name _____

 **Draw** **Color**

 **Directions:** Draw a line from the subject to the correct predicate. Color the pictures. Then use a complete sentence to tell what happens in each pair of pictures.

 **School + Home** **Home Activity:** Help your child write a complete sentence for each pair of pictures.

© Pearson Education, Inc., K

**270 Conventions** Complete Sentences

Name _____

✏️ Write   🖍️ Color

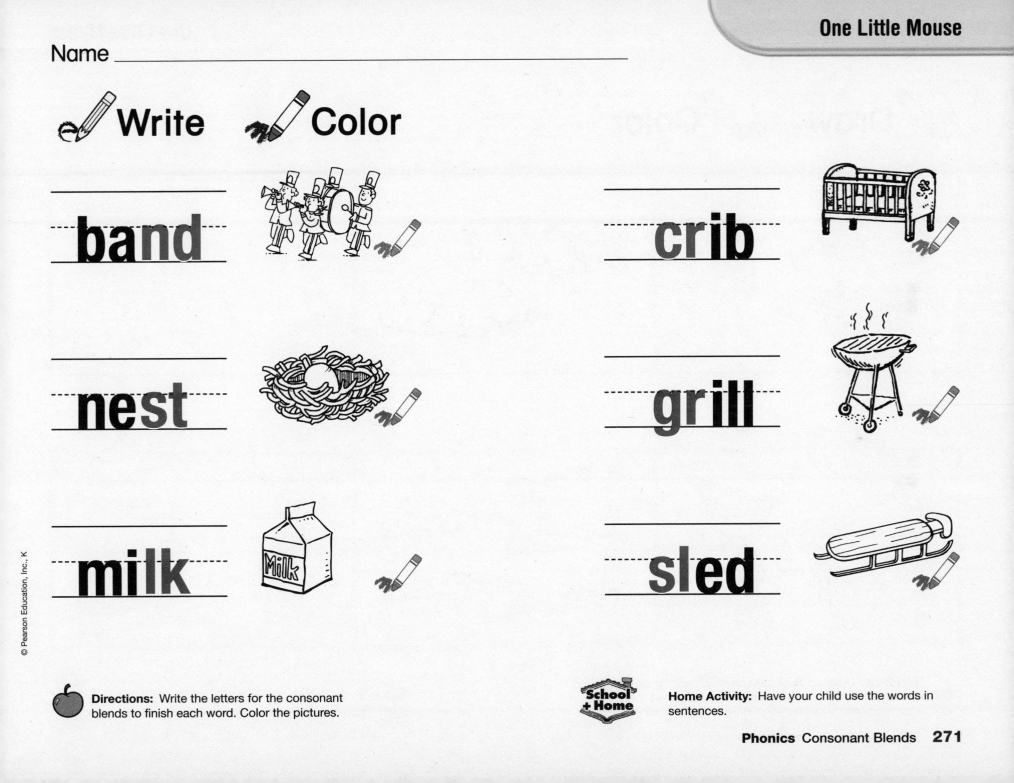

band

nest

milk

crib

grill

sled

© Pearson Education, Inc., K

**Directions:** Write the letters for the consonant blends to finish each word. Color the pictures.

**School + Home**

**Home Activity:** Have your child use the words in sentences.

Name _____

**Draw** **Color**

three frogs

six bunnies

**Directions:** Draw a picture to show which animal the mouse met next. Draw the right number of animals. Color the animals. Then tell what happened in order using words like *first, then next,* and *last.*

**School + Home**

**Home Activity:** Have your child draw pictures of the other animals the mouse met in the correct order.

Name _____

✏️ **Circle** 🖍️ **Color**

Tam (ran) to the spot.

Sam (sits) on the mat.

Bob (hid) in the top.

Lad (hops) to the cat.

© Pearson Education, Inc., K

**Directions** Circle the action part of the sentence and color the picture that shows the action. Then use the action part in a sentence of your own.

**School + Home** **Home Activity** Have your child tell about each picture and name the action part of each one.

**Conventions** Action Parts **273**

Name _____

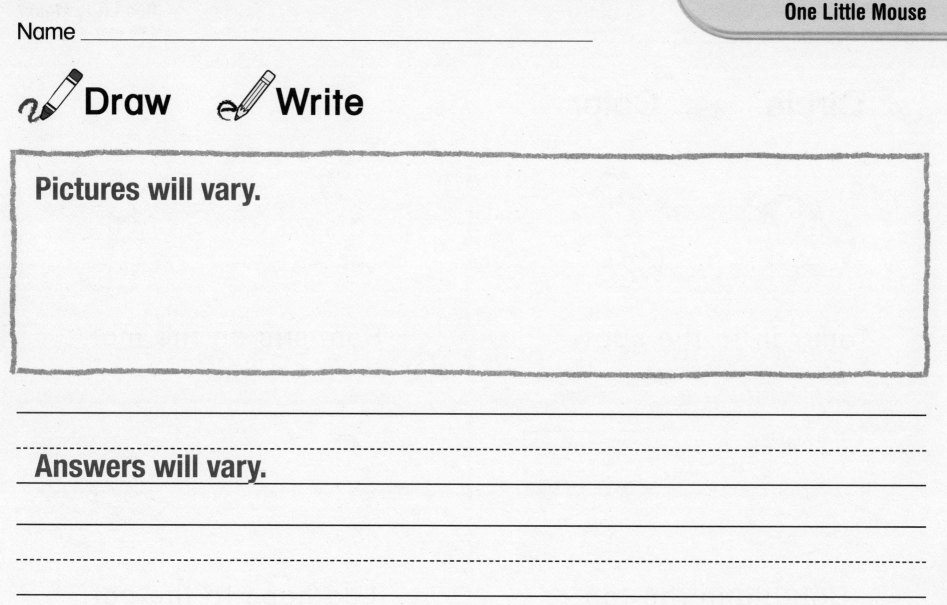

✐ **Draw**    ✐ **Write**

Pictures will vary.

_____

Answers will vary.

_____

_____

 **Directions** Draw a picture of the mouse in the story. Write or dictate a sentence that tells about the animal.

 **School + Home** **Home Activity** Have your child describe things about the mouse in the story.

Name _____

 Circle ✏️ Color

She is _____ .  (mad)  sad

She is _____ .  mad  (sad)

**Directions:** Circle the word to finish the sentence. Color the pictures.

 **Home Activity:** Have your child tell why he or she drew the conclusion he or she did.

Name _____

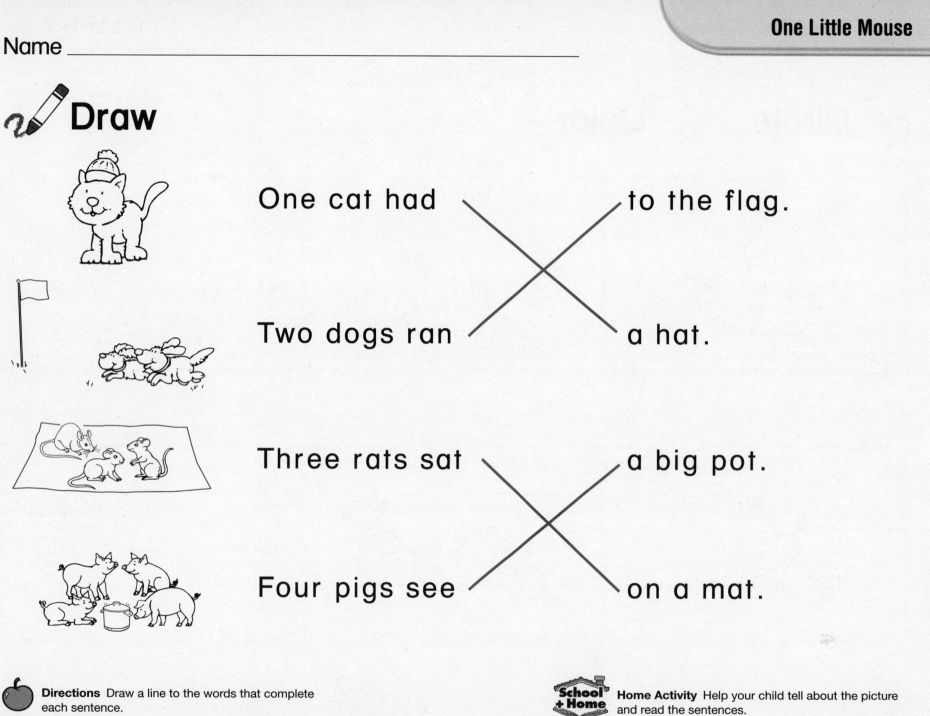

## ✎ Draw

One cat had          to the flag.

Two dogs ran          a hat.

Three rats sat          a big pot.

Four pigs see          on a mat.

🍎 **Directions** Draw a line to the words that complete each sentence.

**School + Home** **Home Activity** Help your child tell about the picture and read the sentences.

Name _____

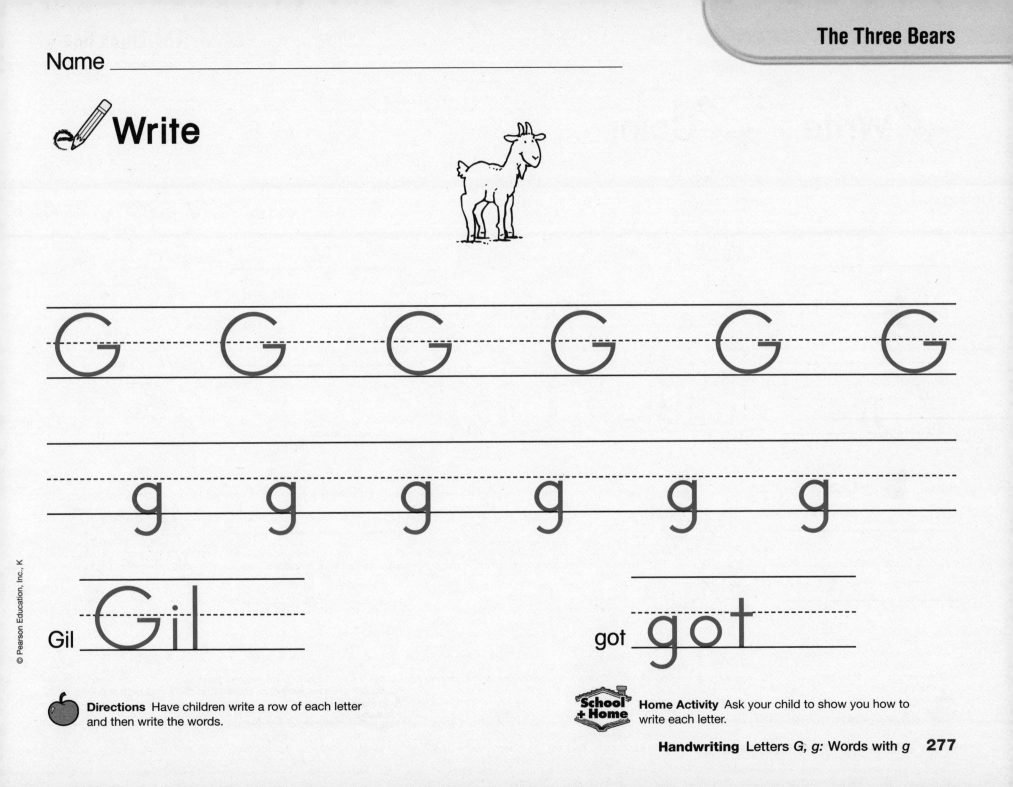

**Write**

G  G  G  G  G  G

g  g  g  g  g  g

Gil **Gil**

got **got**

**Directions** Have children write a row of each letter and then write the words.

**School + Home**

**Home Activity** Ask your child to show you how to write each letter.

Name _____

✏️ **Write**   🖍️ **Color**

**g**   goat

**g**   gate

kite

**Gg**

**g**   gorilla

lamp

**g**   garden

 **Directions:** Name each picture. Write *g* on the line if the word begins with /g/. Color the /g/ pictures.

**School + Home** **Home Activity:** Have your child find pictures that begin with /g/ and paste the pictures on paper to make a /g/ book.

**278** **Phonics** /g/ Spelled *Gg*

© Pearson Education, Inc., K

Can you see four frogs?

Lin and Hap can see
five frogs.

# How Many?

Lin and Hap can see
one dog.

Lin and Hap can see
two kids.

Lin and Hap can see
three pigs.

Name _____

✏️ **Write**   🖍️ **Color**

one   two   three   four   five

I can see _____ **two** _____.

I can see _____ **five** _____.

I can see _____ **four** _____.

I can see _____ **three** _____.

🍎 **Directions:** Read each sentence. Write the missing word to finish the sentence. Color the picture.

© Pearson Education, Inc., K

**School + Home** **Home Activity:** Have your child use the number words in sentences to tell about things in your home.

Name _____

 Draw  Color

| The dog can nab it. | The pig is big. | The cat had one hat. | The log is little. |

 **Directions:** Draw a line from the sentence to the picture it tells about. Then point to and tell about the naming and action parts of the sentence shown in the picture. Color the pictures.

 **Home Activity:** Ask your child to make another statement that tells about each picture.

© Pearson Education, Inc., K

Name _____

✏️ Write    🖍️ Color

goat

dog

bed

gate

leg

cap

gum

pig

**Directions:** Write the letter to finish each word. Color the pictures that begin or end with /g/.

**School + Home**

**Home Activity:** Have your child name the pictures that begin with /g/.

Name _____

# Color

© Pearson Education, Inc., K

**Directions:** Look at the top picture. Color the characters from *Goldilocks and the Three Bears* in the boxes.

 **Home Activity:** Have your child tell about what is happening in the top picture.

Name _____

✏️ **Draw**

A frog sat          to dig.

The pigs like       on a log.

Gil has            the top.

Nan likes        a big hat.

**Directions** Draw a line to the words that complete each sentence.

**School + Home**

**Home Activity** Help your child tell about the picture and read the sentences.

**Conventions** Complete Sentences    **285**

Name _____

 Write

1. **Answers will vary.**

2.

3.

**Directions** Write or dictate a list of things found in the story.

**Home Activity** Help your child write a list. It could be a job list or list of things to do.

Name _____

 Draw  Color

**Picture should show a park.**

**Picture should show a water hole in the jungle.**

**Directions:** Tell a story about the first box. Then draw the setting in the box.

 **Home Activity:** Have your child tell you about the setting for each story.

Name _____

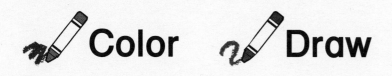
# Color   Draw

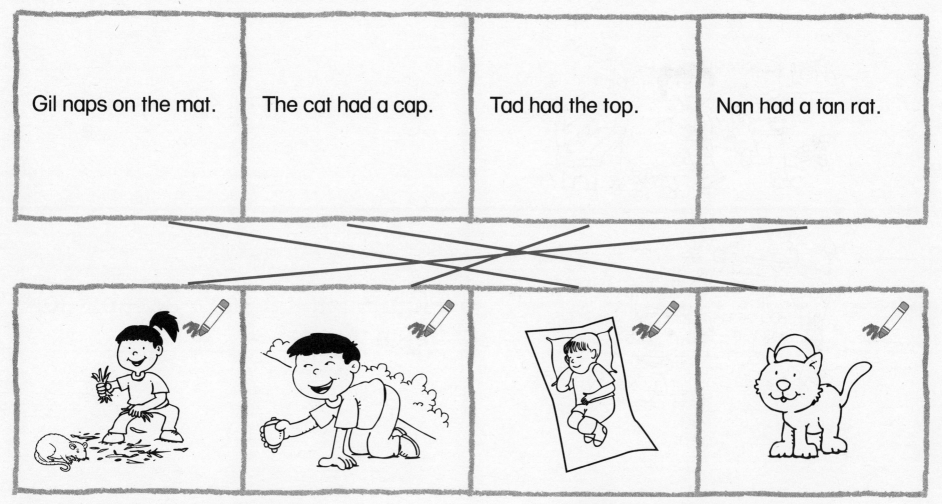

| | | | |
|---|---|---|---|
| Gil naps on the mat. | The cat had a cap. | Tad had the top. | Nan had a tan rat. |

**Directions:** Draw a line from the sentence to the picture it tells about. Color the pictures, then tell another sentence about each picture.

**Home Activity:** Have your child create sentences about people he or she knows.

**288**   **Conventions** Telling Sentences

Name _____

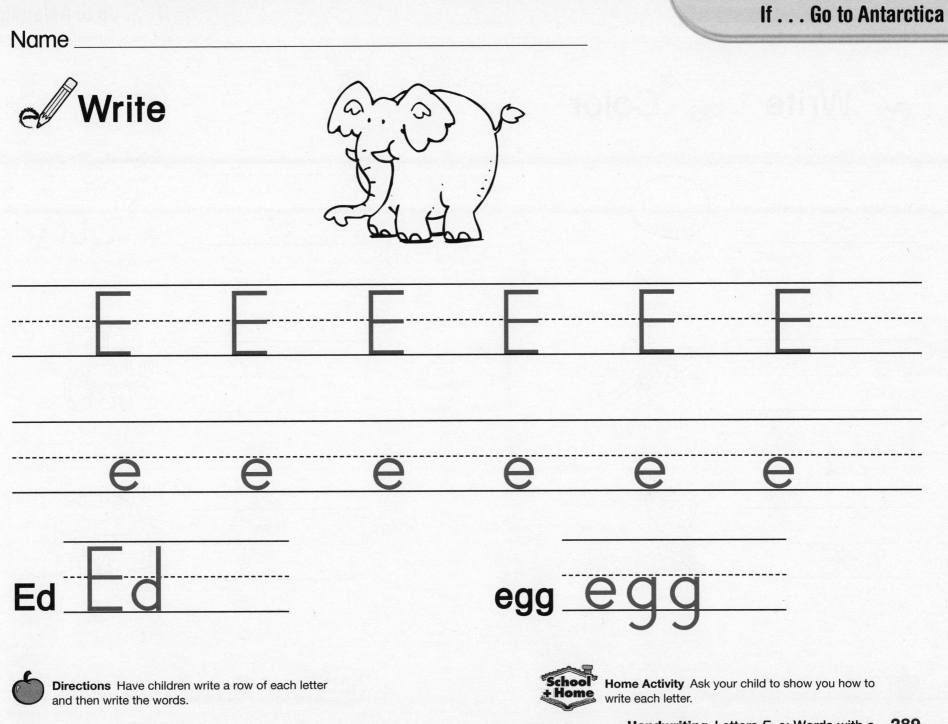

✏️ **Write**

E E E E E E

e e e e e e

**Ed** Ed

**egg** egg

🍎 **Directions** Have children write a row of each letter and then write the words.

🏠 **School + Home** **Home Activity** Ask your child to show you how to write each letter.

Name _____

✏️ **Write**     🖍️ **Color**

_____

e     egg

_____

octopus

_____

e     elf

**Ee**

_____

e     elephant

_____

e     engine

_____

igloo

 **Directions:** Name each picture. Write *e* on the line if the word begins with /e/. Color the /e/ pictures.

 **Home Activity:** Look through a newspaper or book with your child and point out words that begin with /e/.

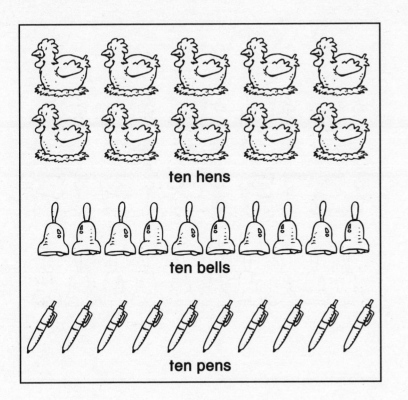

ten hens

ten bells

ten pens

I see ten, ten, ten!

4

**Decodable Story** *Ten, Ten, Ten!*
**Target Skill** /e/ Spelled *Ee*

# Ten, Ten, Ten!

I have a pet hen.

Do you see my hen?

I can see ten.

1

I have a fat pen.

Do you see my pen?

I can see ten.

I have a red bell.

Do you see my bell?

I can see ten.

Name _____

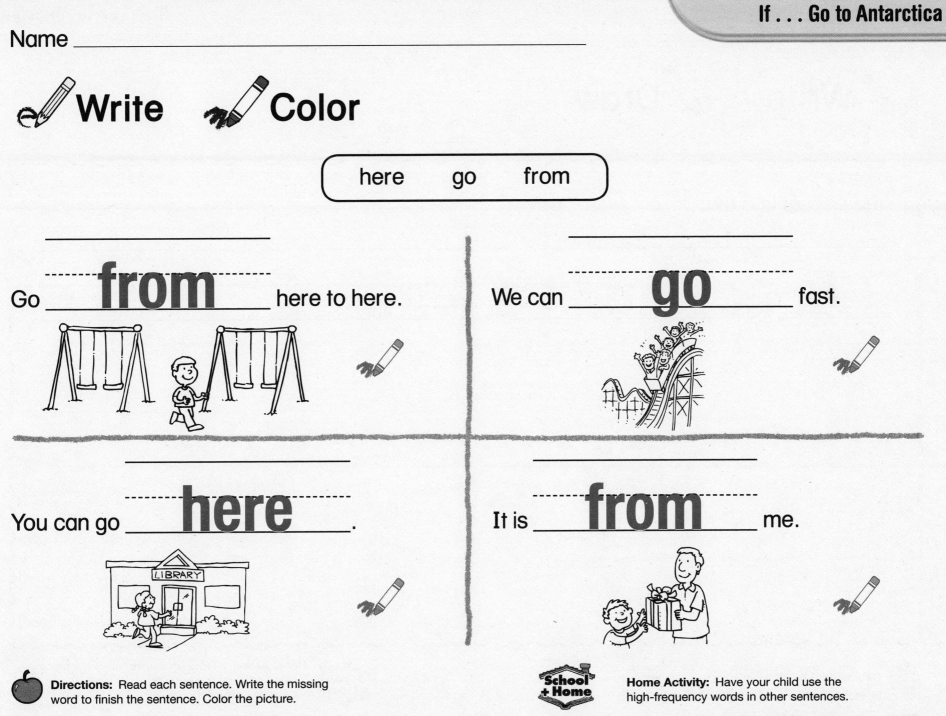

Write      Color

here      go      from

Go __**from**__ here to here.

We can __**go**__ fast.

You can go __**here**__.

It is __**from**__ me.

**Directions:** Read each sentence. Write the missing word to finish the sentence. Color the picture.

School + Home

**Home Activity:** Have your child use the high-frequency words in other sentences.

Name _____

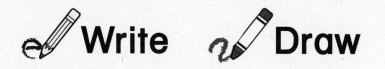 **Write** **Draw**

the pet sat in a tent

**The pet sat in a tent.**

**Directions:** Write the sentence using an uppercase letter and a period. Draw a picture for the sentence.

 **Home Activity:** Write sentences without uppercase letters and periods. Have your child write the sentences correctly.

Name _____

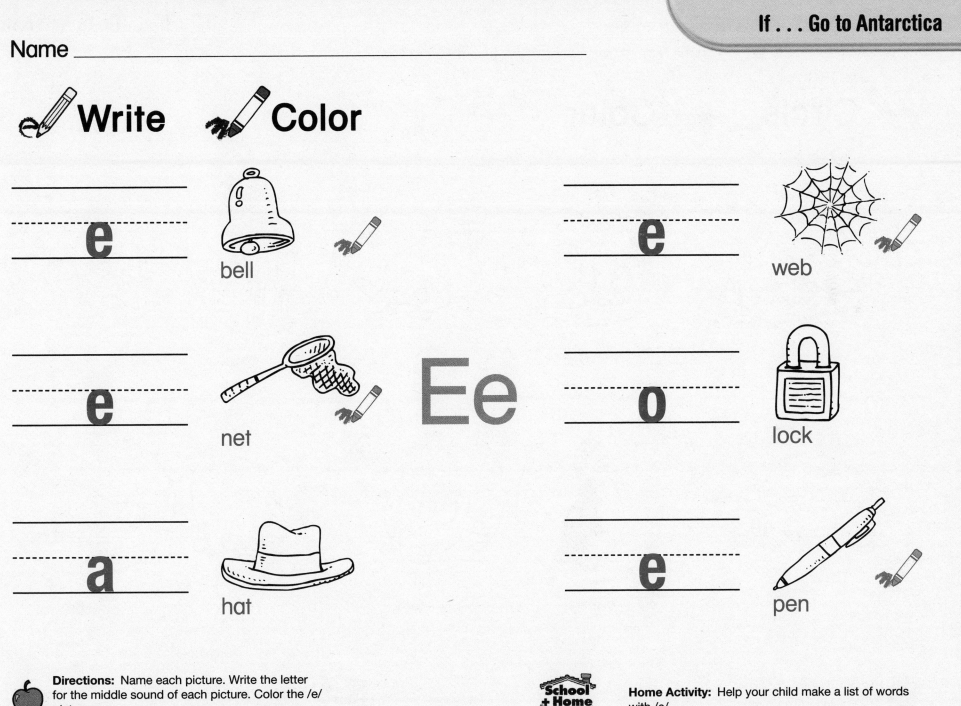

✏️ Write ✏️ Color

e — bell

e — net

a — hat

**Ee**

e — web

o — lock

e — pen

**Directions:** Name each picture. Write the letter for the middle sound of each picture. Color the /e/ pictures.

School + Home

**Home Activity:** Help your child make a list of words with /e/.

Name _____

**Directions:** Circle things that belong together. Color those pictures in each row.

**Home Activity:** Have your child draw three things that belong to the same group—toys, foods, or clothes.

Name _____

✏️ **Draw**

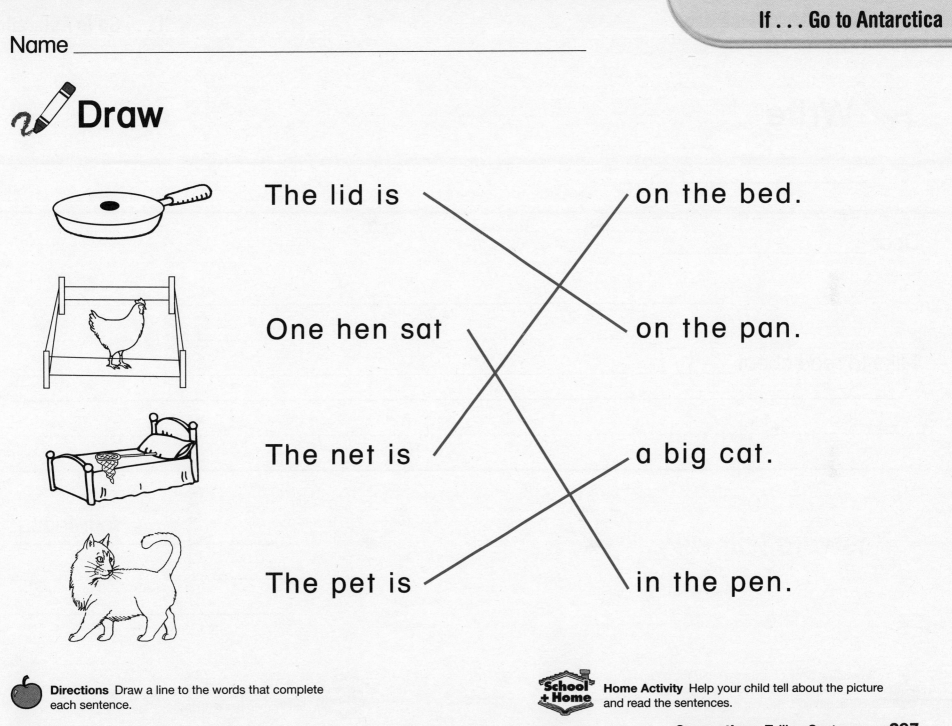

The lid is ......................... on the bed.

One hen sat ....................... on the pan.

The net is ......................... a big cat.

The pet is ......................... in the pen.

🍎 **Directions** Draw a line to the words that complete each sentence.

🏠 **School + Home**  **Home Activity** Help your child tell about the picture and read the sentences.

Name _____

✏️ **Write**

_____

- - - - - - - - - - - - - - - - - - - - - -

Dear _____ ,

_____

- - - - - - - - - - - - - - - - - - - - - - - - - - - - - - -

I like to read about _____

_____

- - - - - - - - - - - - - - - - - - - - - - - - - - - - - - -

_____

Your friend,

**Answers will vary.**

_____

- - - - - - - - - - - - - - - - - - - - - - - - - - - - - - -

_____

🍎 **Directions** Write or dictate a letter to someone. Finish the sentence that tells what you like to read about and then write your name.

🏫 **School + Home** **Home Activity** Help your child write a letter to a family member or friend.

Name _____

# ✏️ Draw

Picture will vary.

🍎 **Directions:** Draw your own picture to show what *If You Could Go to Antartica* is all about.

**School + Home** **Home Activity:** Have your child tell about his or her picture.

Name _____

✏️ **Write**   🖍️ **Draw**

my pet has a net

My pet has a net.

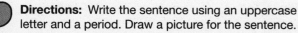
**Directions:** Write the sentence using an uppercase letter and a period. Draw a picture for the sentence.

**300    Conventions** Uppercase Letters and Periods

**Home Activity:** Point to and read sentences in a book and have your child identify the uppercase letter and the period. Ask your child to copy one of the sentences.

© Pearson Education, Inc., K

Name _____

✏️ **Write**

E E E E E

e e e e e

**bed** bed

**hen** hen

**net** net

**pet** pet

**Directions:** Have children write a row of each letter and then write the words.

**School + Home** **Home Activity:** Ask your child to show you how to write each letter.

**Handwriting** Letters *E, e:* Words with *e*  **301**

Name _____

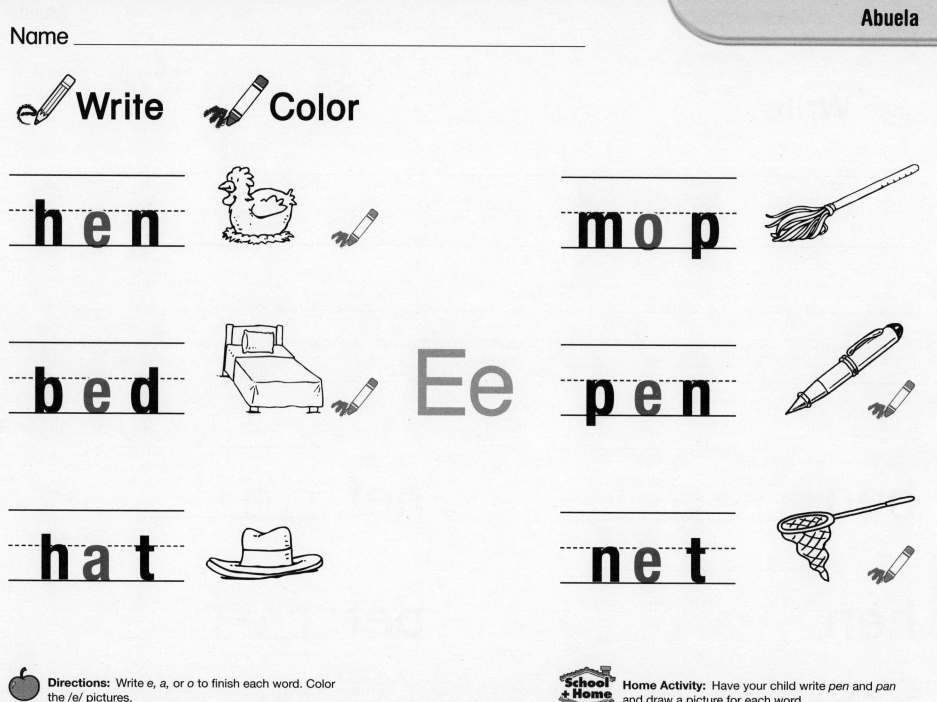

✏️ Write   🖍️ Color

h e n

b e d

h a t

E e

m o p

p e n

n e t

🍎 **Directions:** Write *e, a,* or *o* to finish each word. Color the /e/ pictures.

**School + Home** **Home Activity:** Have your child write *pen* and *pan* and draw a picture for each word.

You can see the tent.

You can see the nest.

I have a pet.

# Ted and the Pet

I am Ted.

I have a pet.

My pet is big.

I met my pet here.

My pet is in the tent.

It is a big tent.

My pet can go to the tent.

My pet has a nest in
the tent.

It is a big nest.

Name _____

 **Draw**

## Pictures will vary.

**Directions:** Have children draw pictures of things to do in the community as list ideas.

 **Home Activity:** Ask your child to tell you about his or her pictures of things to do in the community.

Name _____

 **Draw** **Write**

Pictures and answers will vary.

_____
- - - - - - - - - - - - - - - - - - - - - - - - - -
_____
_____
- - - - - - - - - - - - - - - - - - - - - - - - - -
_____

 **Directions** Have children illustrate the class list topic and dictate or write a question about the topic.

 **Home Activity** Ask your child to tell you about the list the class is planning to write.

Name _____

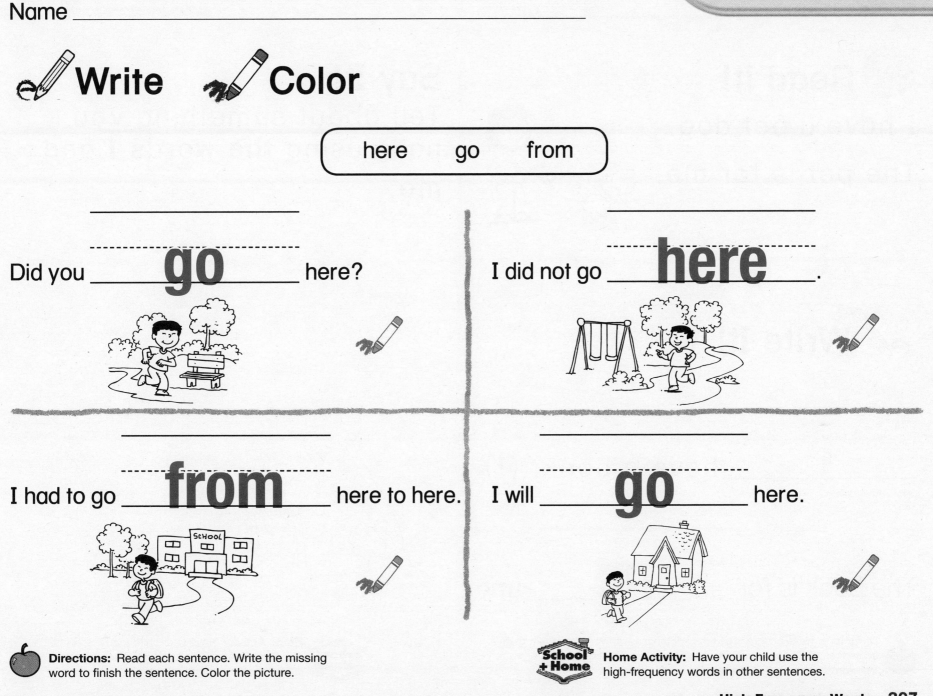

✎ Write    🖍 Color

here    go    from

_____
Did you ___**go**___ here?

_____
I did not go ___**here**___.

_____
I had to go ___**from**___ here to here.

_____
I will ___**go**___ here.

**Directions:** Read each sentence. Write the missing word to finish the sentence. Color the picture.

**School + Home**

**Home Activity:** Have your child use the high-frequency words in other sentences.

Name _____

 **Read It!**

I have a pet dog.

The pet is for me.

**Say It!**

Tell about something you have using the words **I** and **me.**

---

 **Write It!**

_____

------**I**------ have a book. (I)

_____

The book is for _____**me**_____. (me)

**Directions** Have children read the sentences with you. Ask them to give sentences for things they have using *I* and *me*. Then have children write the words *I* and *me* to complete the sentences.

**School + Home** **Home Activity** Have your child read the sentences and find the pronouns *I* and *me*. Then have him or her create sentences with the pronouns *I* and *me*.

**308** **Conventions** Pronouns *I* and *Me*

Name _____

 **Circle**

# Answers will vary.

 **Directions:** Ask: Which sources would you use to find out about tomorrow's weather in our community? Have children circle the best source(s) for that information and then tell why.

 **Home Activity:** Discuss with your child ways that TV can be a good source of information.

Name _____

 Circle  Draw

# Answers will vary.

**Directions:** Ask: Which source or sources would you use to find something new to do in our community? Have children circle the best source(s) for that information. In the empty space have them draw another source they could use to answer the question. Discuss their choices.

**Home Activity:** Suggest various types of information and have your child tell where to look for the information.

**310  Writing Process** Sources

Name _____

✏️ **Circle**   🖍️ **Color**

| | | | |
|---|---|---|---|
| (bed) <br><br> bad | [bed image] | bet <br><br> (bat) | [bat image] |
| log <br><br> (leg) | [leg image] | (pen) <br><br> pan | [pen image] |

 **Directions:** Circle the word that names the picture.
Color the /e/ pictures.

 **Home Activity:** Have your child draw a picture of
something with /e/.

**Phonics** /e/ Spelled *Ee*   311

© Pearson Education, Inc., K

Name _____

 Draw  Color

grocery store

park

 **Directions:** Draw a picture in the last box that tells where the story happened. Color the pictures.

 **Home Activity:** Draw a picture of where and when one of your favorite stories happened.

Name _____

 Write  Draw

the hen likes the pen
_____
- - - - - - - - - - - - - - - - - - - - - - - - - - - - - - - - - - - - -

The hen likes the pen.
_____

 **Directions:** Write the sentence using an uppercase letter and a period. Draw a picture for the sentence.

 **Home Activity:** Point to and read sentences in a book. Have your child identify the uppercase letter and the period. Then help your child create several sentences.

**Conventions** Uppercase Letters and Periods   **313**

Name _____

✏️ Write    🖍 Draw

_____

1. _____

_____

2. _____

_____

3. _____

## Answers will vary.

**Directions** Have children write, dictate, or copy their draft or key words from the class list. Have them draw pictures for the words in your list.

 **School + Home** **Home Activity** Ask your child to tell you what he or she learned about the topic of the class list.

Name _____

 # Color

**Directions:** Color the pictures that show something real.

**Home Activity:** Have your child draw a picture of a real ocean.

Name _____

 **Read It!**

I have a cat.

The cat is for me.

**Say It!**

Tell about something you have using the words **I** and **me**.

---

 **Write It!**

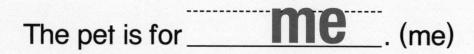

_____ have a pet. (I)

The pet is for _____**me**_____. (me)

**Directions** Have children read the sentences with you. Ask them to give sentences for things they have using *I* and *me*. Then have children write the words *I* and *me* to complete the sentences.

 **Home Activity** Have your child read the sentences and find the pronouns *I* and *me*. Then have him or her create sentences with the pronouns *I* and *me*.

Name _____

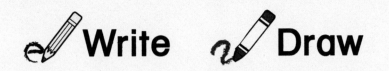 Write    Draw

I will add this to my draft.

_____

- - - - - - - - - - - - - - - - - - - - - - - - - - - - - - - - -

_____

_____

- - - - - - - - - - - - - - - - - - - - - - - - - - - - - - - - -

**Pictures and answers will vary.**

_____

**Directions** Have children draw pictures of and write or dictate additional information that could be included in the class list.

 **School + Home** **Home Activity** Have your child tell you how the class revised the list to make it better.

Name _____

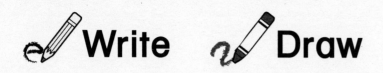 Write  Draw

Pictures and answers will vary.

 **Directions** Have children draw, write, or dictate the entire class list.

 **School + Home** **Home Activity** Discuss with your child another topic he or she would like to write about. Try drafting a list on this topic.

**318** **Writing Process** Revising

Name _____

✏ Circle  ✏ Write

1. you (cango) swimming in Lake (Michigan).

_____

- - - - - - - - - - - - - - - - - - - - - - - - - - -

_____

2. you (can) (see) animals at (twobig) zoos.

_____

- - - - - - - - - - - - - - - - - - - - - - - - - - -

_____

3. you (can) (eat) deep-(dishpizza.)

_____

- - - - - - - - - - - - - - - - - - - - - - - - - - -

_____

 **Directions** Read the sentences together. Help children find the errors. Have them circle the mistakes and rewrite the words or sentences correctly on the lines.

 **Home Activity** Have your child point out and explain his or her edits.

Name _____

✏ Circle    ✏ Write

I shared my selection with ____ **Answers will vary.** ____.

Here's what he/she learned.

_____

- - - - - - - - - - - - - - - - - - - - - - - - - - - - - - -

_____

- - - - - - - - - - - - - - - - - - - - - - - - - - - - - - -

**Directions** Have children circle the picture that shows with whom they shared their list. Then have children ask the peer or adult reviewer to fill in the blanks and to discuss the list with him or her.

**Home Activity** Ask your child to read or tell the class list to you.

Name _____

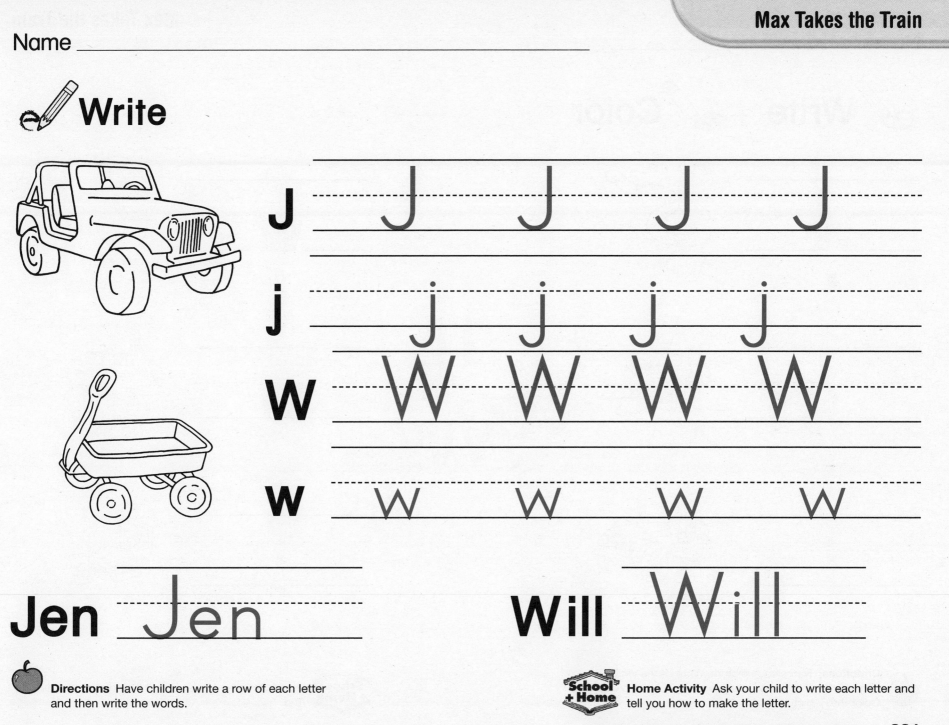

✏️ **Write**

J J J J J

j j j j j

W W W W W

w w w w w

**Jen** Jen

**Will** Will

🍎 **Directions** Have children write a row of each letter and then write the words.

**School + Home** **Home Activity** Ask your child to write each letter and tell you how to make the letter.

Name _____

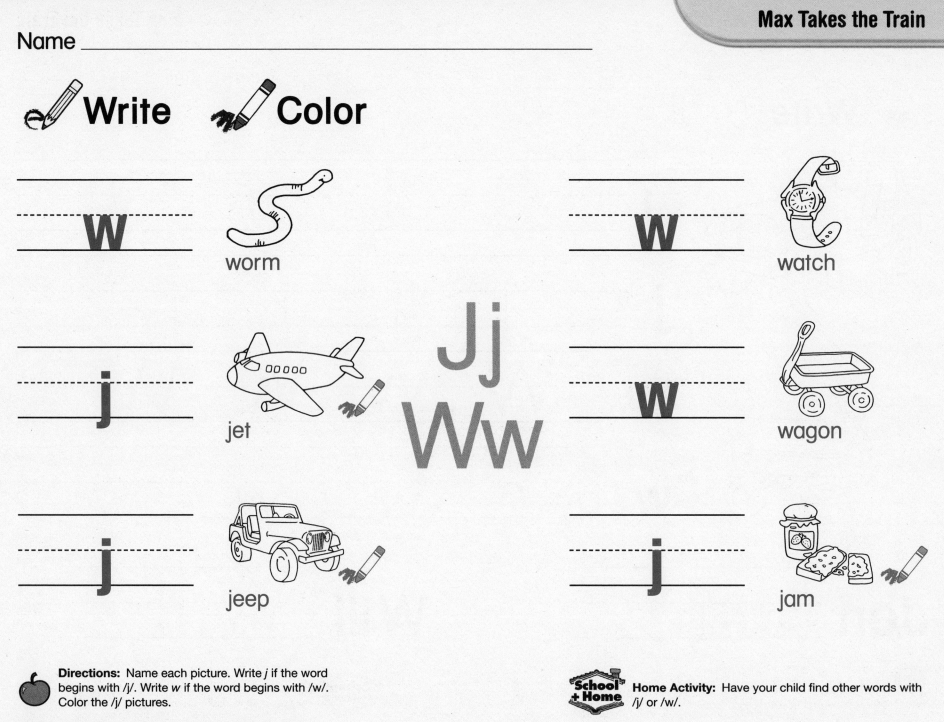

✏ **Write**   ✏ **Color**

w   worm

w   watch

j   jet

**Jj**
**Ww**

w   wagon

j   jeep

j   jam

**Directions:** Name each picture. Write *j* if the word begins with /j/. Write *w* if the word begins with /w/. Color the /j/ pictures.

**School + Home**   **Home Activity:** Have your child find other words with /j/ or /w/.

You can get on the big, blue jet.

You can go with Jen and Will.

# Jen and Will

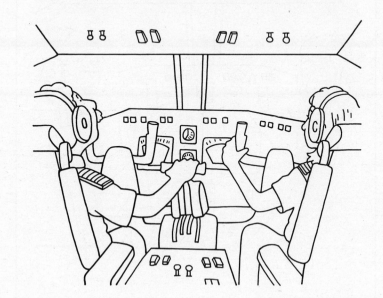

Jen and Will get on the jet.

It is a big, blue jet.

Jen and Will have jobs
on the jet.

Jen and Will like the jobs.

Jen and Will get the jet
to go.

They can see you.

Name _____

✏️ Write   🖍️ Color

yellow    blue    green    have

_____

The pond is _____ **blue** _____ .

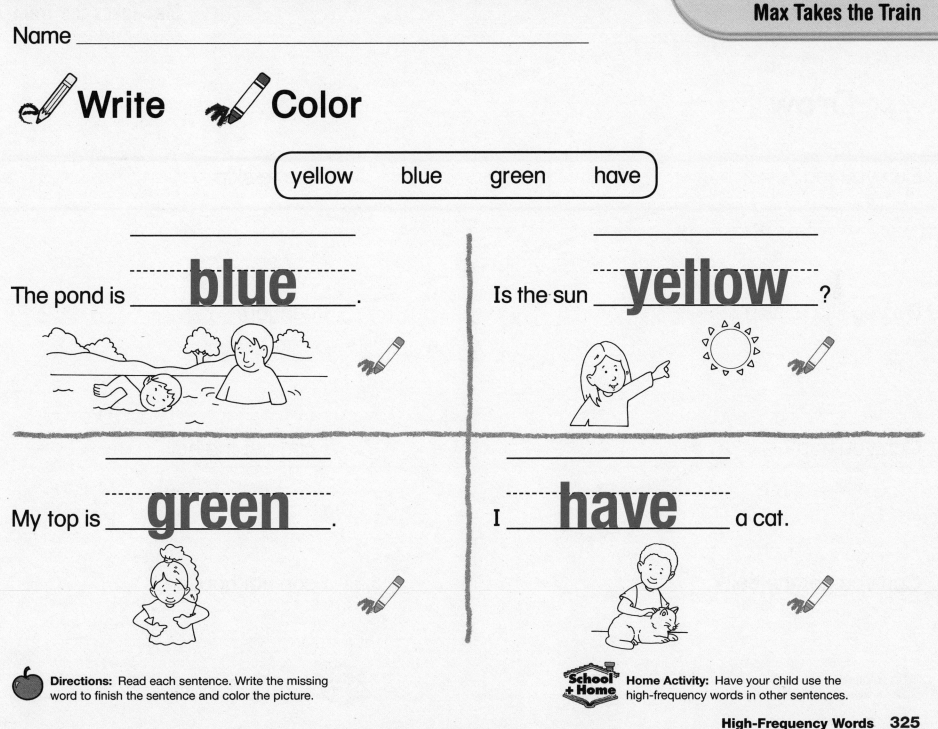

_____

Is the sun _____ **yellow** _____ ?

_____

My top is _____ **green** _____ .

_____

I _____ **have** _____ a cat.

🍎 **Directions:** Read each sentence. Write the missing word to finish the sentence and color the picture.

**School + Home** **Home Activity:** Have your child use the high-frequency words in other sentences.

**High-Frequency Words**   **325**

© Pearson Education, Inc., K

Name _____

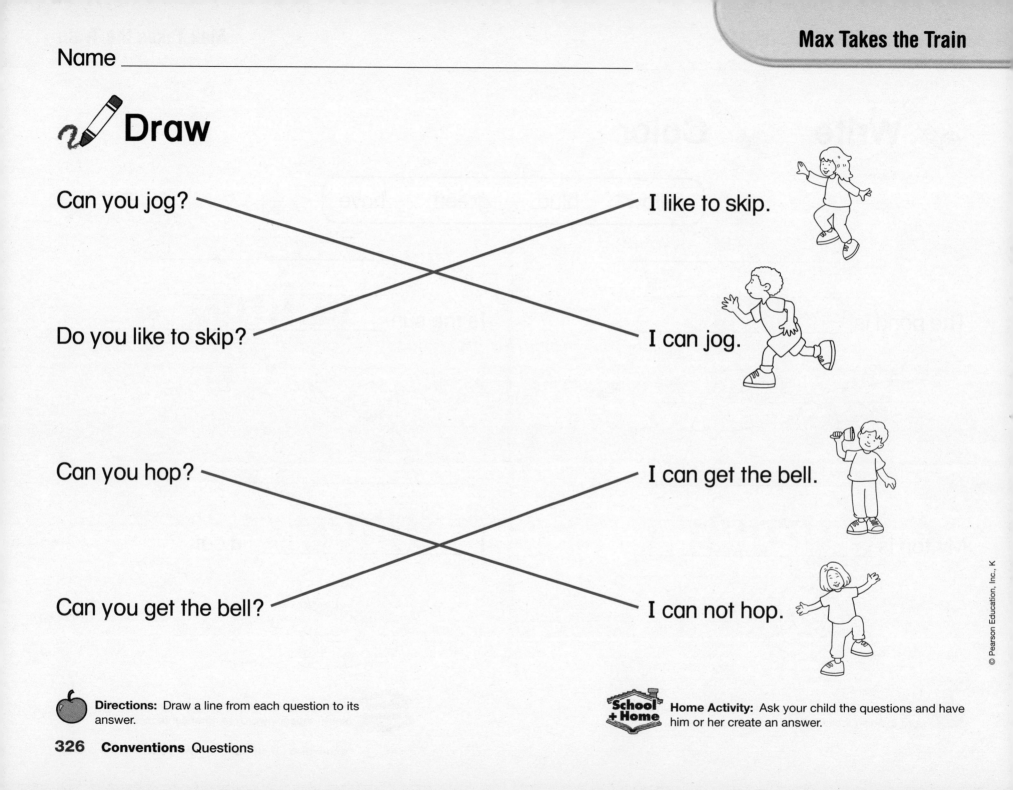

✏️ **Draw**

Can you jog?

I like to skip.

Do you like to skip?

I can jog.

Can you hop?

I can get the bell.

Can you get the bell?

I can not hop.

**Directions:** Draw a line from each question to its answer.

**Home Activity:** Ask your child the questions and have him or her create an answer.

Name _____

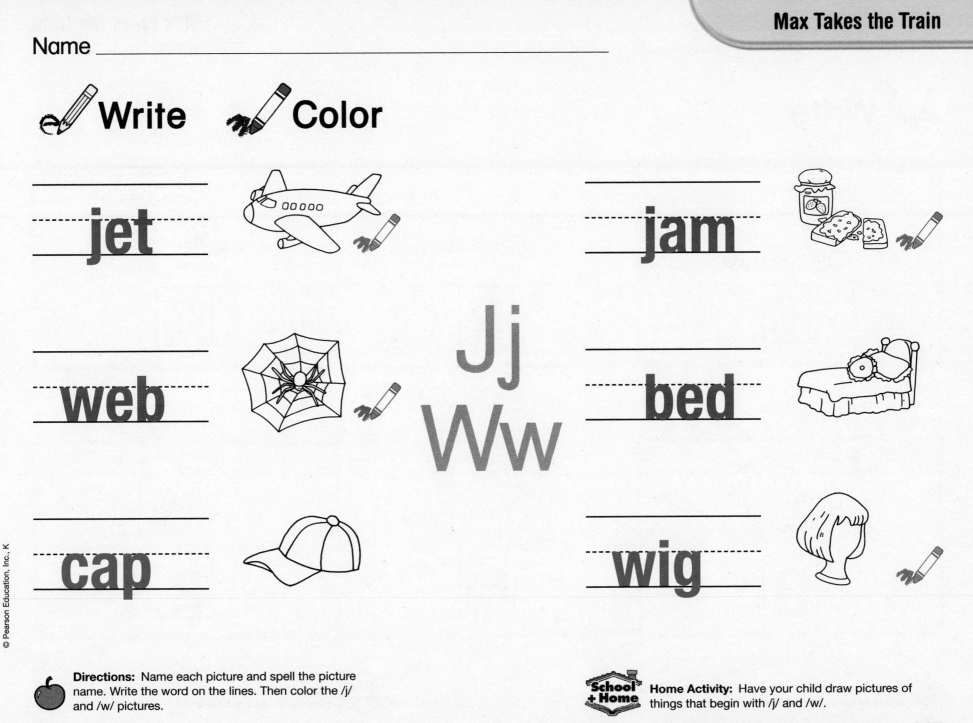

✏️ Write   🖍️ Color

jet

jam

web

**Jj**
**Ww**

bed

cap

wig

**Directions:** Name each picture and spell the picture name. Write the word on the lines. Then color the /j/ and /w/ pictures.

**School + Home** **Home Activity:** Have your child draw pictures of things that begin with /j/ and /w/.

Name _____

✏️ **Write**

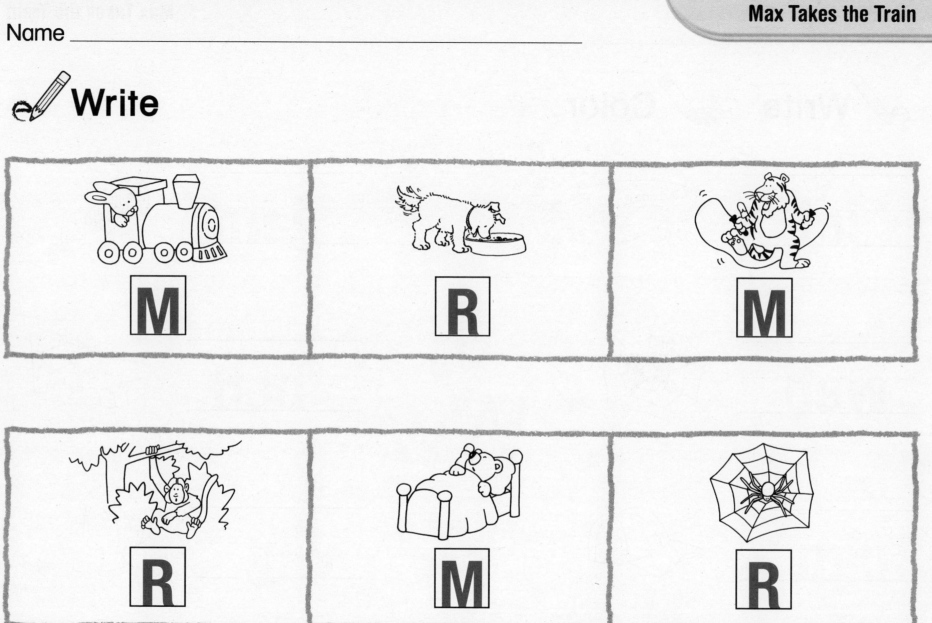

**Directions:** Label the animal in each picture *R* for real or *M* for make-believe.

© Pearson Education, Inc., K

**Home Activity:** Have your child draw and color a picture of a real animal and where it lives.

Name _____

 # Read It!

I have a box.

The box is for me.

# Say It!

Tell about something you have using the words **I** and **me**.

---

 # Write It!

_____

_____**I**_____ have a bat. (I)

_____

The bat is for _____**me**_____. (me)

 **Directions** Have children track the print and read the sentences with you. Ask children to say sentences for things they have using *I* and *me*. Then have children write the pronouns *I* and *me* to complete the sentences.

 **Home Activity** Have your child read the sentences and find the pronouns *I* and *me*. Then have him or her create sentences with the pronouns *I* and *me*.

Name _____

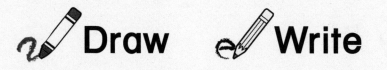 **Draw** **Write**

Pictures and answers will vary.

 **Directions** Have children draw a picture of an animal home. Have them use content-based vocabulary, such as social studies words, to write or dictate a caption for their picture.

 **Home Activity** Show pictures and have your child think of a caption for each picture.

**330 Writing** Caption

Name _____

# ✏️ Number

| 2 | 3 | 1 |

 **Directions** Write the numbers 1, 2, and 3 to tell what happened at the beginning, in the middle, and near the end of *Max Takes the Train*.

 **Home Activity** Have your child tell the story using the pictures.

Name _____

 Circle  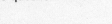 Draw

Where is the fan?
The fan is by the mat.

The dog is on the big bed.
What is big?

Where is the book?
Jen set the book on the box.

Then hen is in the pen.
Where is the hen?

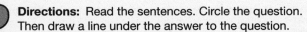 **Directions:** Read the sentences. Circle the question.
Then draw a line under the answer to the question.

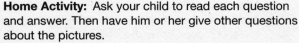 **Home Activity:** Ask your child to read each question
and answer. Then have him or her give other questions
about the pictures.

© Pearson Education, Inc., K

Name _____

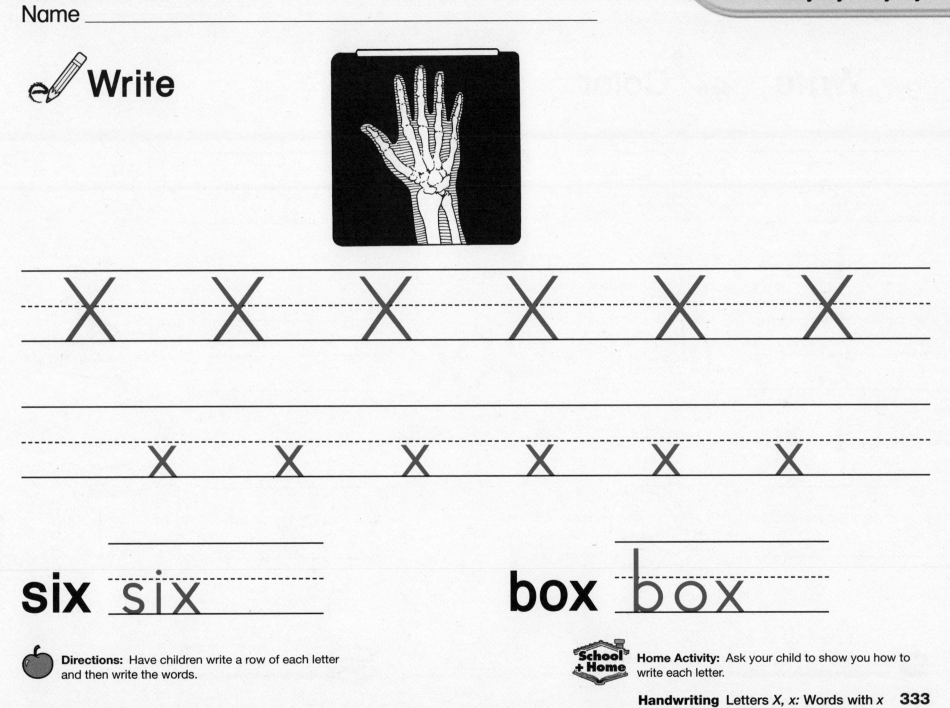

✏ **Write**

X X X X X X

x x x x x x

**six** six

**box** box

**Directions:** Have children write a row of each letter and then write the words.

**Home Activity:** Ask your child to show you how to write each letter.

Name _____

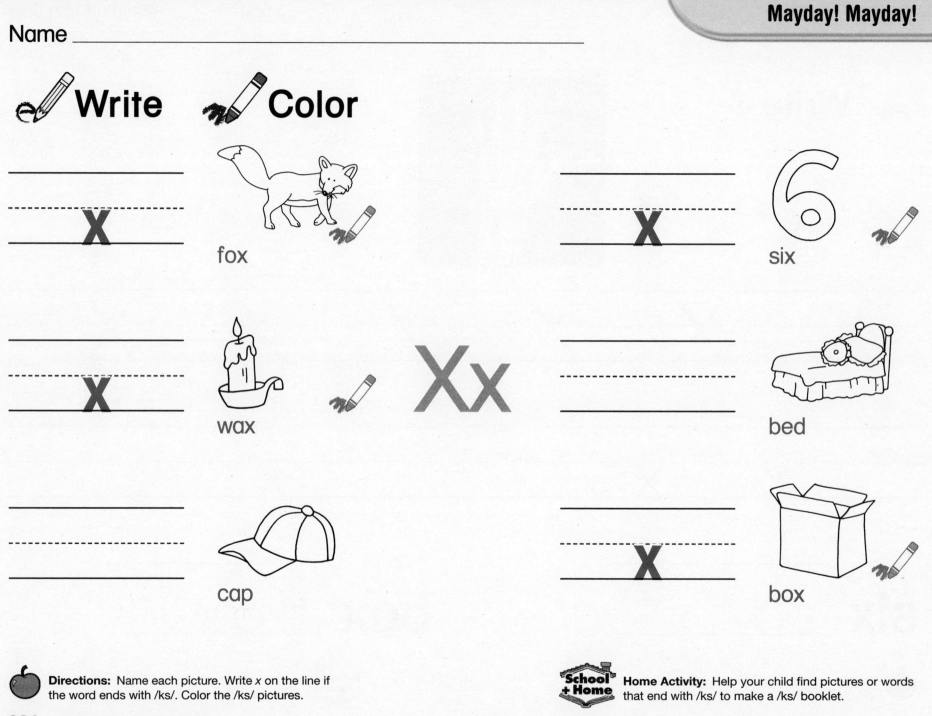

## ✏️ Write   🖍️ Color

x — x

fox

x — x

wax

— —

cap

**Xx**

x — x

six

— —

bed

x — x

box

🍎 **Directions:** Name each picture. Write *x* on the line if the word ends with /ks/. Color the /ks/ pictures.

**School + Home** **Home Activity:** Help your child find pictures or words that end with /ks/ to make a /ks/ booklet.

Max can see his pal Rex.

Max and Rex can mix
yellow and red.

4

**Decodable Story** *Max*
**Target Skill** /ks/ Spelled *Xx*

# Max

Max is six.

He hid in a box.

He hid from his mom.

1

Max can look like a fox.

He has four legs.

Max can mix blue and green.

It is an ox.

Name _____

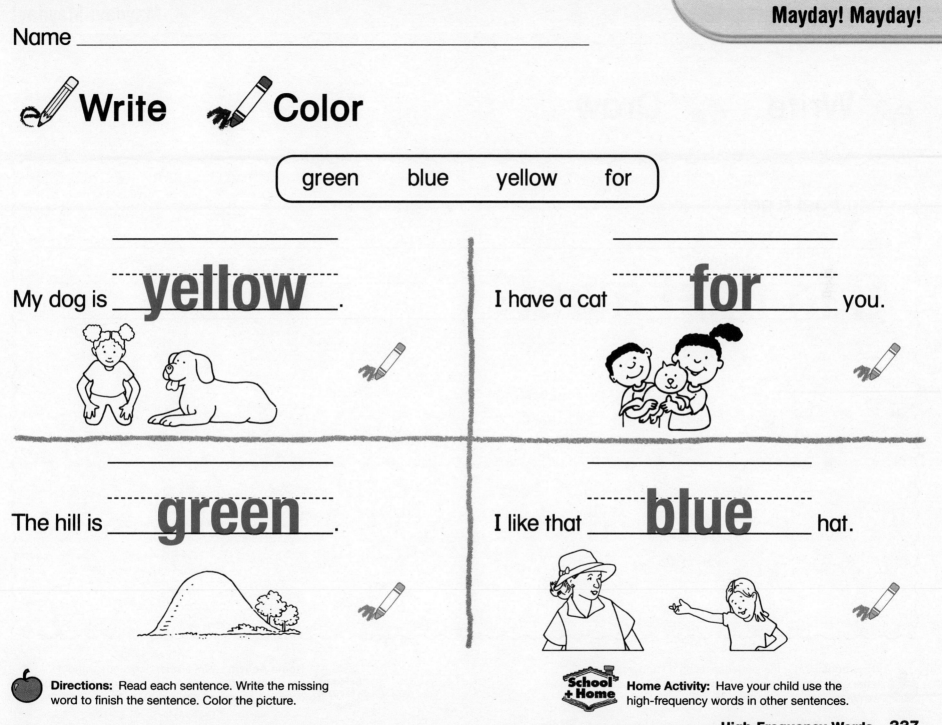

✏️ **Write**    🖍️ **Color**

| green    blue    yellow    for |

_____

My dog is _____ **yellow** _____.

The hill is _____ **green** _____.

I have a cat _____ **for** _____ you.

I like that _____ **blue** _____ hat.

🍎 **Directions:** Read each sentence. Write the missing word to finish the sentence. Color the picture.

**School + Home** **Home Activity:** Have your child use the high-frequency words in other sentences.

© Pearson Education, Inc., K

Name _____

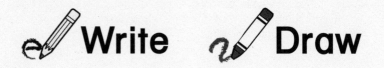 Write  Draw

can I get a pet

# Can I get a pet?

 **Directions:** Write the sentence using an uppercase letter and a question mark. Draw a picture for the sentence.

 **Home Activity:** Write other questions without uppercase letters and question marks. Have your child write the questions correctly.

Name _____

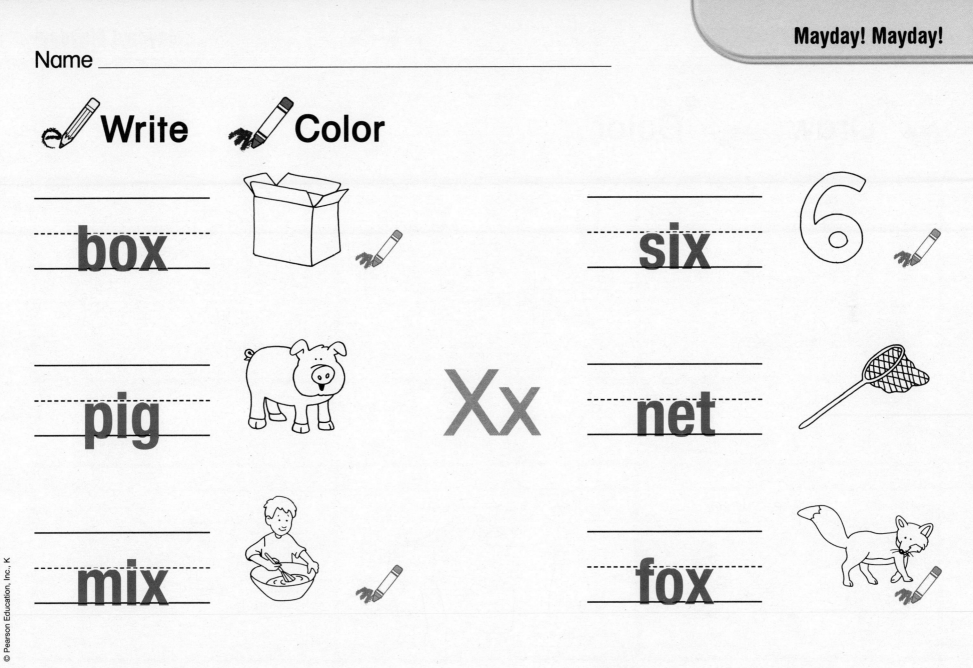

✏️ Write    🖍️ Color

box

pig

mix

Xx

six

net

fox

**Directions:** Name each picture and spell the picture name. Write the word on the lines. Then color the pictures that end with /ks/.

**Home Activity:** Have your child draw a picture of something that ends with /ks/.

**Phonics** /ks/ Spelled *Xx*    339

Name _____

 Draw ✏️ Color

 **Directions:** Draw a line from what happened to why it happened. Color each picture.

 **School + Home**  **Home Activity:** Have your child tell you what happened in each picture and why it happened.

Name _____

/ **Circle**   / **Color**

I see a cat.

Do you see a cat?

Do you see Nan?

I see Nan.

What can Tim hit?

Tim hits the lid.

Lad can hop.

What can Lad do?

© Pearson Education, Inc., K

**Directions:** Circle the question. Underline the answer. Then color the pictures.

**Home Activity:** Have your child read each question and answer. Then help them say and write other questions and answers.

Name _____

✏️ **Write** 🖍️ **Draw**

---
- - - - - - - - - - - - - - - - - - - - - - - -
---
---
- - - - - - - - - - - - - - - - - - - - - - - -
---

**Pictures will vary.**

🍎 **Directions** Have children copy the rhyme about saving the boat. Then have them draw a picture of it.

 **School + Home** **Home Activity** Help your child make a poem with rhyming words such as *boat, goat, coal,* and *float*.

Name _____

 **Write**

**Directions:** Number the boxes to show what happens first, next, and last in each story. Then retell the story using the words *first, next,* and *last.*

 **School + Home**

**Home Activity:** Ask your child to draw three pictures that show how to make a sandwich.

**Comprehension** Sequence **343**

Name _____

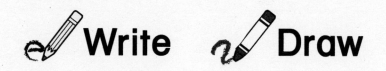 Write  Draw

where can I get a pet

_____

## Where can I get a pet?

## Pictures will vary.

 **Directions:** Write the sentence using an uppercase letter and a question mark. Draw a picture for the sentence.

 **Home Activity:** Choose a variety of topics and help your child create questions and answers about the topic.

**344** **Conventions** Question Marks and Uppercase Letters

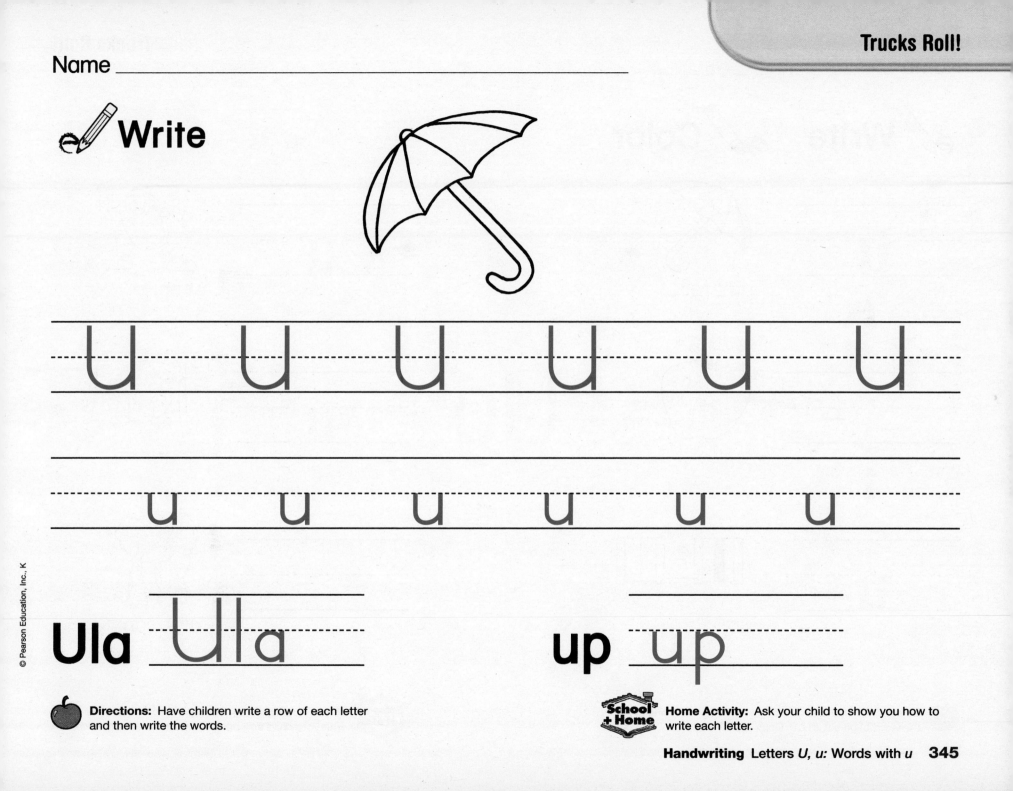

Name _____

✏️ **Write**

u u u u u u u

u u u u u u

**Ula** Ula

**up** up

🍎 **Directions:** Have children write a row of each letter and then write the words.

**School + Home** **Home Activity:** Ask your child to show you how to write each letter.

**Handwriting** Letters *U, u*: Words with *u*   **345**

Name _____

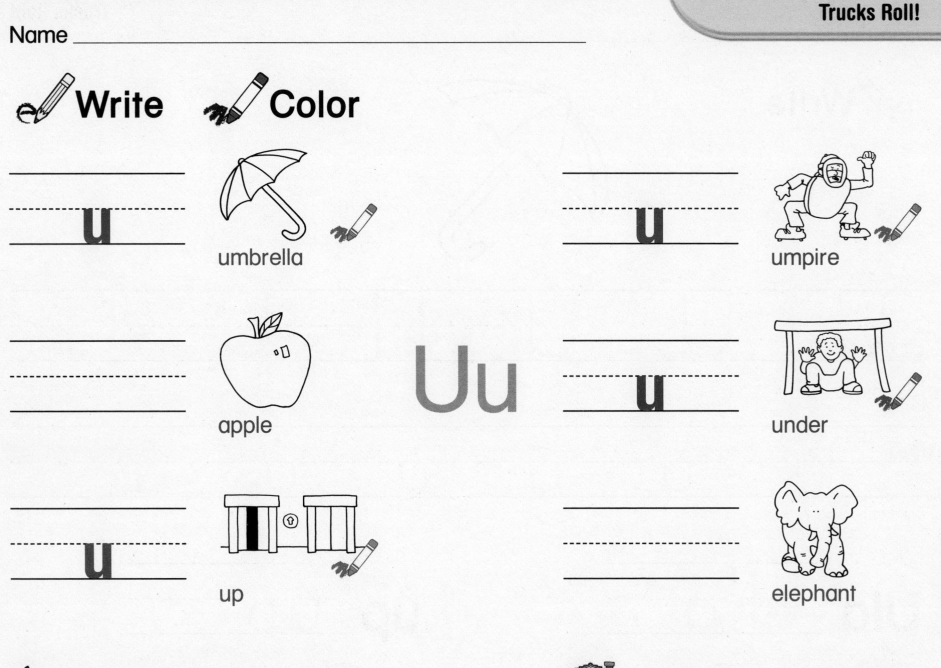

✏️ **Write**      🖍️ **Color**

u        umbrella

         apple

u        up

**Uu**

u        umpire

u        under

         elephant

**Directions:** Name each picture. Write *u* on the line if the word begins with /u/. Color the /u/ pictures.

 **School + Home**   **Home Activity:** Look through a newspaper or book with your child and point out words that begin with /u/.

Jud ran to his pals.

Jud said, "Let us go in!

We will have fun!"

**Decodable Story** *Fun for Jud*
**Target Skill** /u/ Spelled *Uu*

# Fun for Jud

The sun was hot.

Jud got up from bed.

Jud has to have a plan.

What can he do for fun?

Jud will see his pals.

What will they do for fun?

Name _____

✏️ **Write**   🖍️ **Color**

what    was    said    she

_____

**Was** _____ she with you?

_____

He _____ **said** _____ she was with me.

_____

**She** _____ is my mom.

_____

**What** _____ did you see?

🍎 **Directions:** Read each sentence. Write the missing word to finish the sentence. Color the picture.

**School + Home** **Home Activity:** Have your child use the high-frequency words in other sentences.

**High-Frequency Words  349**

© Pearson Education, Inc., K

Name _____

 **Read It!**

The pet is on the box.

**Say It!**

Say a sentence about a cat

using the word **in**.

 **Write It!**

**by the book**

_____

The dog sat ____**by**____ the book.

 **Directions** Have children track the print and read the sentence with you. Ask them to say a sentence about a cat with the word *in*. Then have children write the preposition *by* to complete the sentence.

 **Home Activity** Have your child create sentences using the prepositions *on, in,* or *by*.

**350** **Conventions** Prepositions

Name _____

✏️ Write    🖍️ Color

bus

cup

hen

Uu

rug

pig

nut

**Directions:** Name each picture and spell the picture name. Write the word on the lines. Then color the /u/ pictures.

**School + Home** **Home Activity:** Help your child make a list of words with /u/.

**Phonics** /u/ Spelled *Uu*    **351**

Name _____

 **Color**

**Directions:** Color each matching pair a different color.

 **Home Activity:** Have your child compare and contrast the bike messengers by telling how the pictures are alike and how they are different.

**352** **Comprehension** Compare and Contrast

Name _____

 Write  Draw

can I see the pet

_____

<u>**Can I see the pet?**</u>

**Pictures will vary.**

 **Directions:** Write the question using an uppercase letter and a question mark. Draw a picture for the sentence.

 **Home Activity:** Write a short question on paper and read the question. Have your child identify the uppercase letter and the question mark. Then help your child create and write another question.

Name _____

 **Write**  ✏️ **Draw**

_____
- - - - - - - - - - - - - - - - - - - -
_____

_____
- - - - - - - - - - - - - - - - - - - -
_____

**Pictures will vary.**

 **Directions** Have children copy the poem about the truck. Then have them draw a picture of the truck.

**School + Home** **Home Activity** Help your child make a poem with rhyming words such as *truck, luck, stuck,* and *duck.*

Name _____

 Circle  Color

 **Directions:** Circle the picture that shows what you think will happen next. Color the pictures.

 School + Home

**Home Activity:** Have your child explain how he or she arrived at each conclusion.

**Comprehension** Draw Conclusions  **355**

Name _____

 **Read It!**

The bug sat on the rug.

**Say It!**

Use **by** in a sentence about something in the room.

 **Write It!**

The bug sat ____**in**____ the tub. (in)

 **Directions** Have children track the print and read the sentence with you. Ask them to say a sentence about something in the room using *by*. Then have children write the preposition *in* to complete the sentence.

 **Home Activity** Point to things and have your child tell where they are, using the prepositions *on, in, near,* or *by—near the table, on the couch, by the door.*

© Pearson Education, Inc., K

Name _____

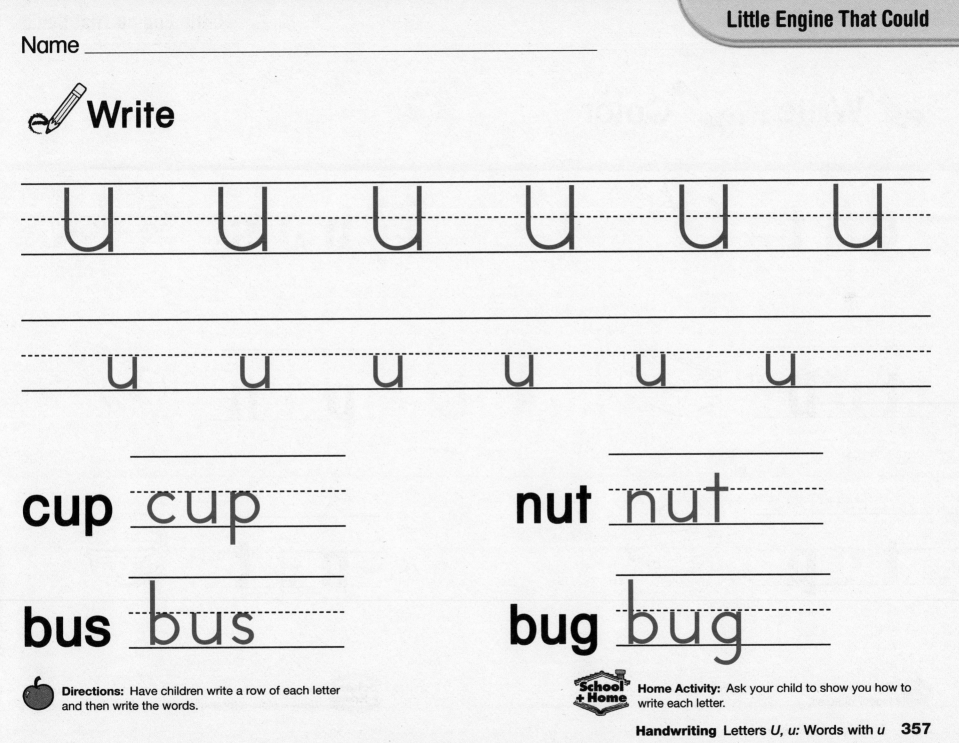

✏ **Write**

U U U U U U U

u u u u u u u

**cup** cup

**nut** nut

**bus** bus

**bug** bug

**Directions:** Have children write a row of each letter and then write the words.

**School + Home** **Home Activity:** Ask your child to show you how to write each letter.

Name _____

✏️ **Write**     🖍️ **Color**

cut

tub

top

Uu

bus

pin

nut

🍎 **Directions:** Write *i*, *o*, or *u* to finish each word. Color the /u/ pictures.

 **Home Activity:** Have your child write *rug* and *bug* and draw a picture for each word.

Jan and Gus are on the rug.

Jan and Gus are pals.

4

**Decodable Story** *Jan and Gus*
**Target Skill** /u/ Spelled *Uu*

# Jan and Gus

Jan and Gus are pals.

They like to have fun.

1

Jan and Gus like the sun.

They like to hum on the bus.

Jan and Gus see a bug.

They run in the mud.

Name _____

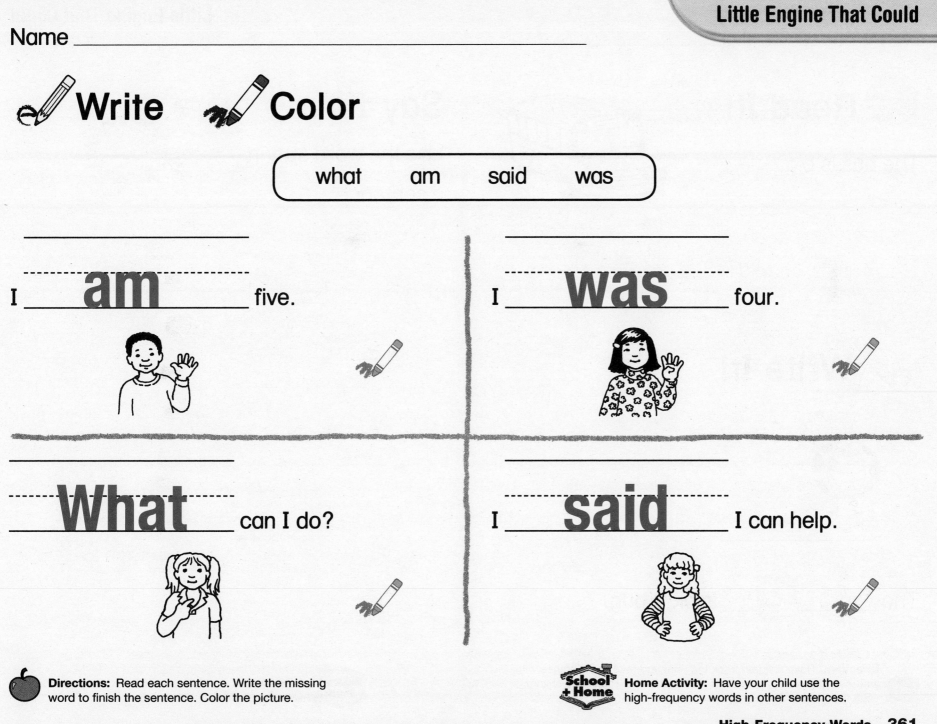

✏️ **Write**     🖍️ **Color**

| what | am | said | was |

_____

I ___**am**___ five.

_____

I ___**was**___ four.

_____

___**What**___ can I do?

_____

I ___**said**___ I can help.

🍎 **Directions:** Read each sentence. Write the missing word to finish the sentence. Color the picture.

**School + Home**  **Home Activity:** Have your child use the high-frequency words in other sentences.

Name _____

 **Read It!**

The bus is big.

**Say It!**

Use the word **sun** in a sentence.

 **Write It!**

The _____**bug**_____ is big. (bug)

 **Directions** Have children track the print and read the sentence with you. Ask them to say a sentence about the sun. Then have children write the noun to complete the sentence.

 **Home Activity:** Have your child use the nouns *bus,* *sun,* and *bug* in other sentences.

Name _____

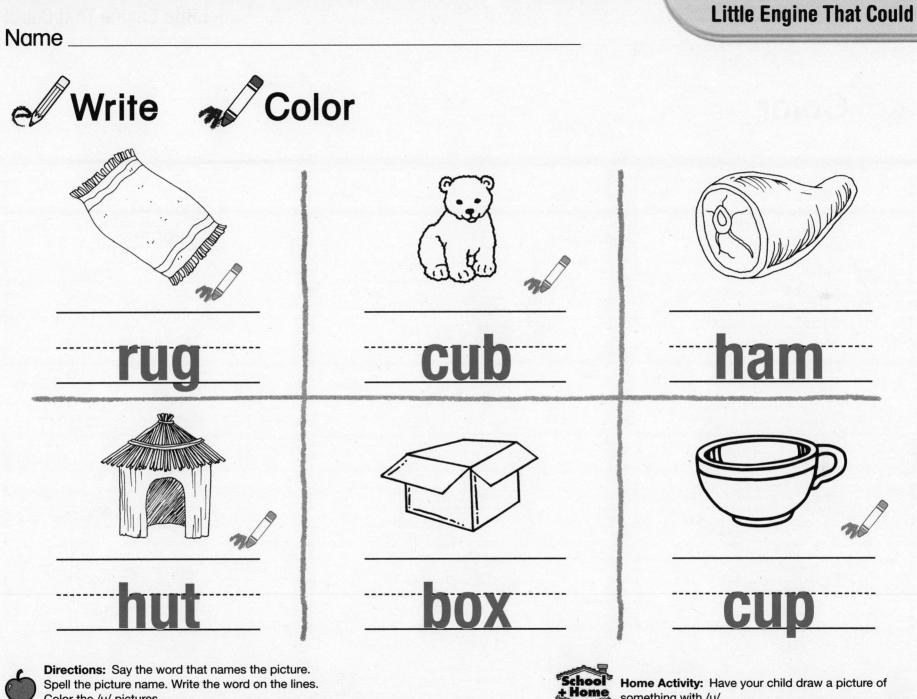

✏️ Write    🖍️ Color

rug

cub

ham

hut

box

cup

**Directions:** Say the word that names the picture. Spell the picture name. Write the word on the lines. Color the /u/ pictures.

**School + Home**

**Home Activity:** Have your child draw a picture of something with /u/.

Name _____

## ✏️ Color

 **Directions:** Color the picture that shows what would happen next in each story.

 **Home Activity:** Have your child tell what he or she does after putting on his or her pajamas.

Name _____

 **Read It!**

The dog is under the table.

**Say It!**

Use the word **on** in a sentence about something in the classroom.

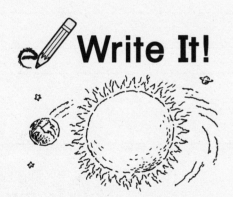 **Write It!**

The sun is _____ **in** _____ the sky. (in)

 **Directions** Have children track the print and read the sentence about the dog. Ask them to say a sentence using the word *on*. Then have children write the preposition to complete the sentence about the sun.

 **Home Activity** Have your child use the prepositions *on, in,* or *under* in sentences. Provide sentence clues as needed.

Name _____

✏️ **Write**

_____

------------------------

Dear _____ ,

_____

------------------------------------------------

_____

_____

_____

------------------------------------------------

**Answers will vary.**

Your friend,

_____

------------------------------------

_____

🍎 **Directions** Have children compose a letter to someone. Have them write or dictate the person's name and a sentence that tells about a toy they like. Then have children write their name.

**School + Home** **Home Activity** Help your child write a letter to a family member or friend.

Name _____

 **Color** **Draw**

woman

dog

**Directions:** Color the pictures. Then draw a picture in the last box that shows who the character in each story is.

**School + Home** **Home Activity:** Have your child draw a picture of the characters in one of his or her favorite stories.

**Comprehension** Character   **367**

Name _____

 **Read It!**

The mug is big.

**Say It!**

Tell something about the bug.
Use the word **bug** in your
sentence.

 **Write It!**

_____

The ____ **sun** ____ is big. (sun)

 **Directions** Have children track the print and read the sentence about the mug. Ask them to tell something about a bug. Then have children write the noun to complete the sentence.

**School + Home** **Home Activity** Have your child give another sentence about each picture.

**368** **Conventions** Nouns

Name _____

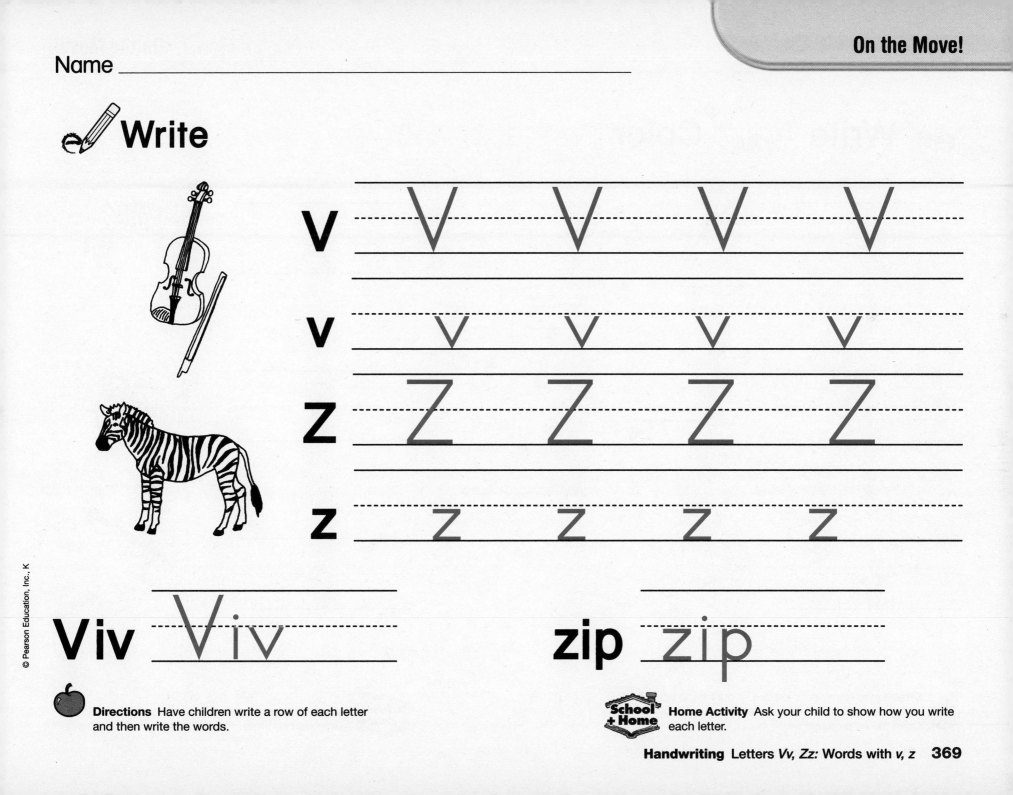

**Write**

V   V V V V

v   v v v v

Z   Z Z Z Z

z   z z z z

**Viv**  Viv

**zip**  zip

**Directions** Have children write a row of each letter and then write the words.

**Home Activity** Ask your child to show how you write each letter.

Name _____

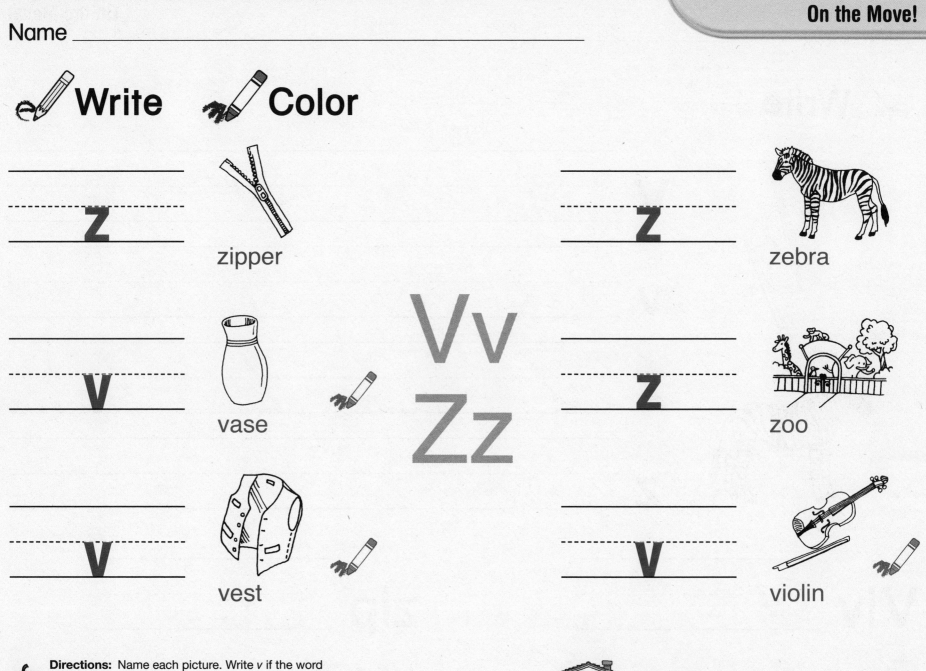

✏️ **Write**    🖍️ **Color**

z

zipper

z

zebra

v

vase

Vv
Zz

z

zoo

v

vest

v

violin

**Directions:** Name each picture. Write *v* if the word begins with /v/. Write *z* if the word begins with /z/. Color the /v/ pictures.

**School + Home** **Home Activity:** Have your child find other words that begin with /v/ or /z/.

He will zap the tag.

Val has got the red top.

**Decodable Story** *Val's Top*
**Target Skill** /v/ Spelled *Vv*, /z/ Spelled *Zz*

# Val's Top

Val and Mom come in a van.

They will go to look for a top.

Val and Mom see a top.

They can zip it up.

The top is red.

Val and Mom like the top.

Name _____

✏️ **Write**     🖍️ **Color**

| where | is | come | me |
|-------|----|----|----|

_____

Do they see ___**me**___ ?

_____

___**Come**___ here, little dog.

_____

___**Where**___ did you go?

_____

My mom ___**is**___ here.

**Directions:** Read each sentence. Write the missing word to finish the sentence. Color the picture.

**School + Home** **Home Activity:** Have your child use the high-frequency words in other sentences.

Name _____

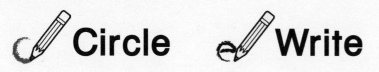 Circle  ✏ Write

leg
run

My **leg** got cut.

sit
pal

This is my **pal**.

pig
big

Come here, little **pig**.

hop
bug

Look at the **bug**.

van
will

That **van** is big.

hit
hill

Run up the **hill**.

🍎 **Directions:** Circle the noun that matches the picture.
Write the word to complete the sentence.

**School + Home**

**Home Activity:** Have your child read each sentence.

© Pearson Education, Inc., K

Name _____

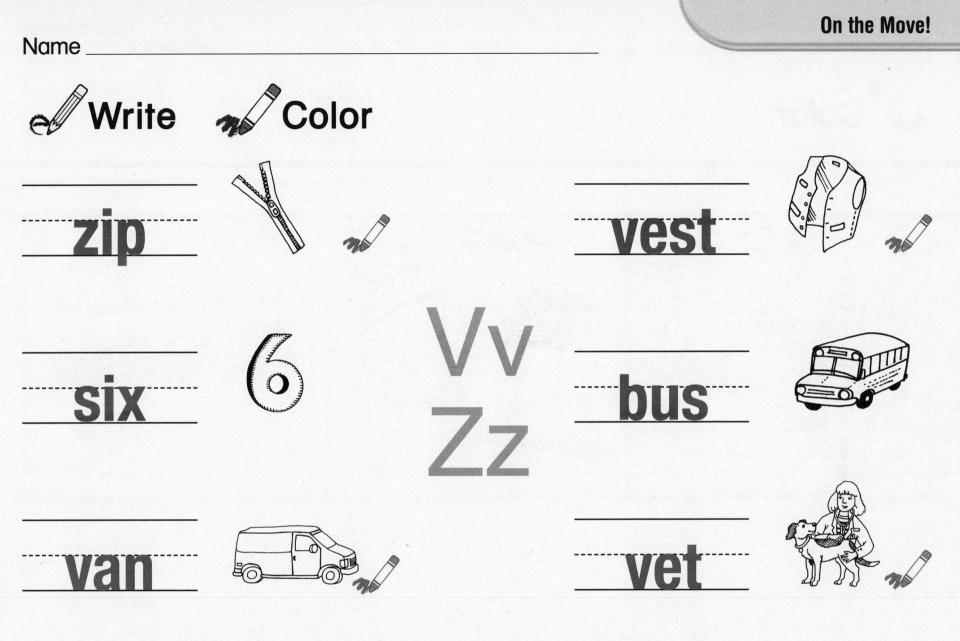

✏️ Write   🖍️ Color

zip

six

van

Vv
Zz

vest

bus

vet

**Directions:** Name each picture and spell the picture name. Write the word on the lines. Then color the /z/ and /v/ pictures.

**School + Home**  **Home Activity:** Have your child draw pictures of things that begin with /v/ and /z/.

Name _____

 Color

**Directions:** Color the picture that shows the main idea of the story *On the Move!*

**Home Activity:** Have your child tell you about the story and why he or she chose the main idea picture. Also have your child tell why the other pictures do not show the main idea.

**376** **Comprehension** Main Idea

Name _____

 **Read It!**

The cub is little.

**Say It!**

Tell something about the tub. Use the word **tub** in your sentence.

 **Write It!**

The _____**nut**_____ is little. (nut)

 **Directions** Have children read the sentence about the cub. Ask them to say a sentence about the tub. Then have children write the noun to complete the sentence.

 **Home Activity** Point to items in the house and have your child name the item and use the word in a sentence.

Name _____

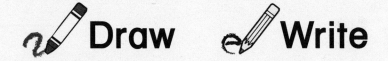 **Draw** **Write**

Pictures and answers will vary.

Come to our play.

_____

It is on _____.

_____

It is at _____ o'clock.

 **Directions** Draw a picture for your class play. Then write or dictate the missing information for the class.

 **Home Activity** Help your child create an invitation to a real or make believe family event.

**378** **Writing** Invitation

Name _____

 **Draw**  **Color**

 **Directions:** Draw a line from what happened to why it happened. Color each picture.

 **Home Activity:** Have your child tell why each event happened.

**Comprehension** Cause and Effect **379**

Name _____

✏ **Circle**   ✏ **Write**

cup
(pup)

_____

The little **pup** is here.

(cat)
rat

_____

The little **cat** ran.

(hen)
pen

_____

One fat **hen** is here.

log
(dog)

_____

The **dog** likes it.

(pet)
net

_____

The little **pet** is wet.

fan
(man)

_____

A cat ran to the **man** .

© Pearson Education, Inc., K

**Directions:** Look at the picture. Read the sentence. Circle the noun to complete the sentence. Write the word.

**School + Home**  **Home Activity:** Have your child use the noun that is not circled in each box in a sentence.

Name _____

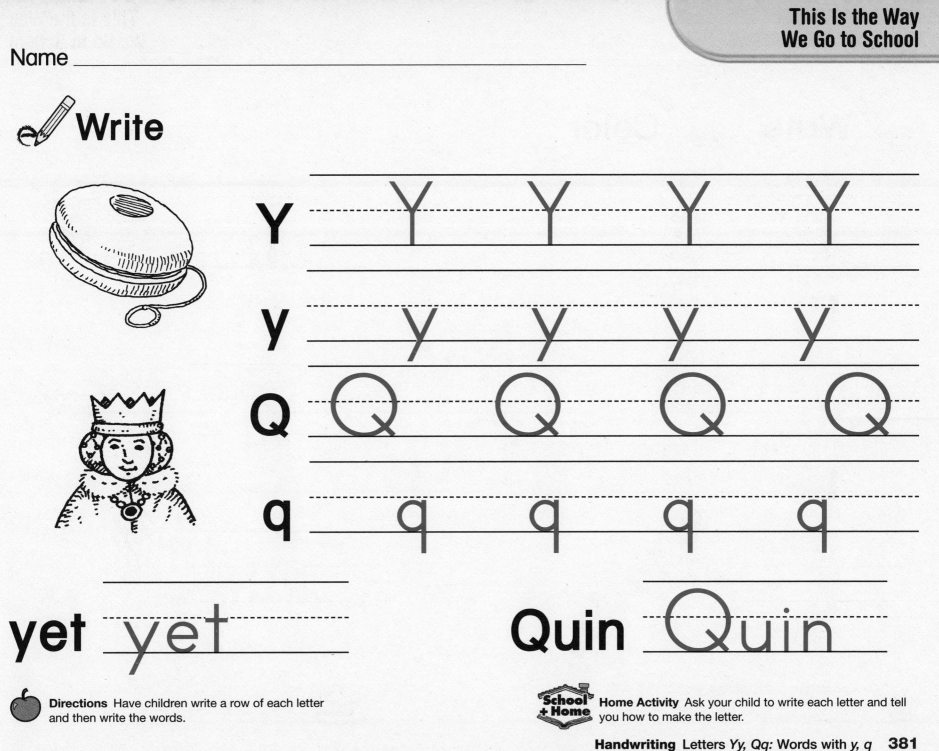

✏️ **Write**

Y    Y    Y    Y    Y

y    y    y    y    y

Q    Q    Q    Q    Q

q    q    q    q    q

**yet**  yet

**Quin**  Quin

🍎 **Directions** Have children write a row of each letter and then write the words.

🏠 **School + Home** **Home Activity** Ask your child to write each letter and tell you how to make the letter.

**Handwriting** Letters *Yy, Qq*: Words with *y, q*  **381**

Name _____

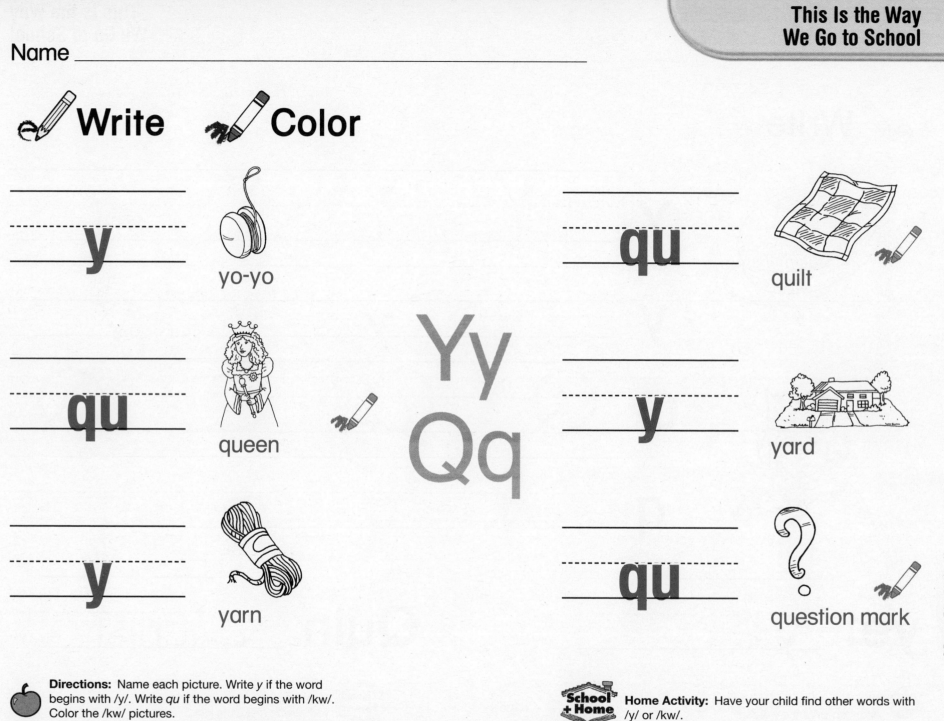

✏️ **Write**     🖍️ **Color**

_____  y     yo-yo

_____  qu     queen

_____  y     yarn

Yy
Qq

_____  qu     quilt

_____  y     yard

_____  qu     question mark

**Directions:** Name each picture. Write *y* if the word begins with /y/. Write *qu* if the word begins with /kw/. Color the /kw/ pictures.

**Home Activity:** Have your child find other words with /y/ or /kw/.

Tim ran to the end.

Tim had a rest.

**Decodable Story** *Run, Tim*
**Target Skill** /y/ Spelled *Yy*, /kw/ Spelled *Qq*

# Run, Tim

Tim ran past his sis.

She said,

"You can not quit yet."

Tim ran up a hill.

His dad said,

"You can not quit yet."

Tim ran and ran.

His mom said,

"You can not quit yet."

Name _____

 **Draw**

**Pictures will vary.**

**Directions** Have children draw pictures of themselves doing or making things as topic ideas for the how-to report.

 **Home Activity** Ask your child to tell you about his or her pictures of topic ideas.

Name _____

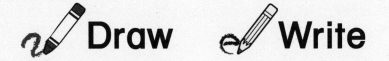 Draw ✎ Write

Pictures and answers will vary.

_____

- - - - - - - - - - - - - - - - - - - - - - - - - - - -

_____

_____

- - - - - - - - - - - - - - - - - - - - - - - - - - - -

_____

 **Directions** Have children illustrate or write the class
how-to report topic question and dictate or write
another question about the topic.

 **Home Activity** Ask your child to tell you about the
how-to report the class is planning to write.

Name _____

✏️ **Write**    🖍️ **Color**

| come | we | where | she |

_____
**She** _____ can see me.

_____
**We** _____ can run fast.

_____
**Where** _____ will you go?

_____
**Come** _____ and see this bug.

🍎 **Directions:** Read each sentence. Write the missing word to finish the sentence. Color the picture.

**School + Home** **Home Activity:** Have your child use the high-frequency words in other sentences.

© Pearson Education, Inc., K

Name _____

✏ Circle   ✏ Write

dog

(sat)

_____

She _____ **sat** on the bus.

(look)

yet

_____

We _____ **look** up at a jet.

hat

(ran)

_____

My dog _____ **ran** to me.

(see)

bag

_____

_____ **See** my cat!

(hop)

leg

_____

He can _____ **hop** .

bell

(sit)

_____

Can I _____ **sit** here?

**Directions:** Circle the verb that matches the picture.
Write the word to complete the sentence.

School
+ Home

**Home Activity:** Have your child read each sentence.

Name _____

# ✏️ Circle

☆ DAILY STAR ☆

Tallahassee and Ft. Worth win recycling awards.

## Circle person at reference desk in library.

**Directions** Ask: Which source would be best to find out how to get a library card? Have children circle the best source and then tell why.

**School + Home** **Home Activity** Discuss with your child ways that the computer can be a good source for information .

Name _____

 Circle  Draw

☆ DAILY STAR ☆

Tallahassee and Ft. Worth win recycling awards.

**Answers will vary.**

**Directions** Ask: Which source or sources would you use to find the hours the library is open? Have children circle the best source(s). In the empty space, have them draw another source they could use to answer the question. Discuss their choices.

**Home Activity** Suggest various types of information and have your child tell where to look for the information.

**390** **Writing Process** Sources

Name _____

✏ Write   🖍 Color

quilt

yarn

quack

Yy
Qq

yak

quick

yell

**Directions:** Name each picture. Write *y* if the word begins with /y/. Write *qu* if the word begins with /kw/. Color the /y/ pictures.

School + Home

**Home Activity:** Have your child draw pictures of things that begin with /y/ and /kw/.

Name _____

 Circle  Color

 **Directions:** Circle the picture that shows what you think the child would do next. Color the pictures.

 **Home Activity:** Have your child explain how he or she arrived at each conclusion.

**392** **Comprehension** Draw Conclusions

Name _____

 Circle    ✐ Write

The box is big.

box

The bus will go fast.

bus

That is a big bed.

bed

 **Directions** Say the picture name. Read the sentence.
Circle the noun. Then write the noun on the lines.

**School + Home**    **Home Activity** Point to and read sentences in a book.
Have your child identify the nouns.

**Conventions** Nouns in Sentences    **393**

Name _____

✏ **Write**    🖍 **Draw**

1. _____

**Answers will vary.**

2. _____

3. _____

**Directions** Have children write, dictate, or copy their draft or key words from the how-to report. Have them draw pictures to go with the list.

**School + Home**  **Home Activity** Ask your child to tell you what he or she learned about the topic of the class how-to report.

Name _____

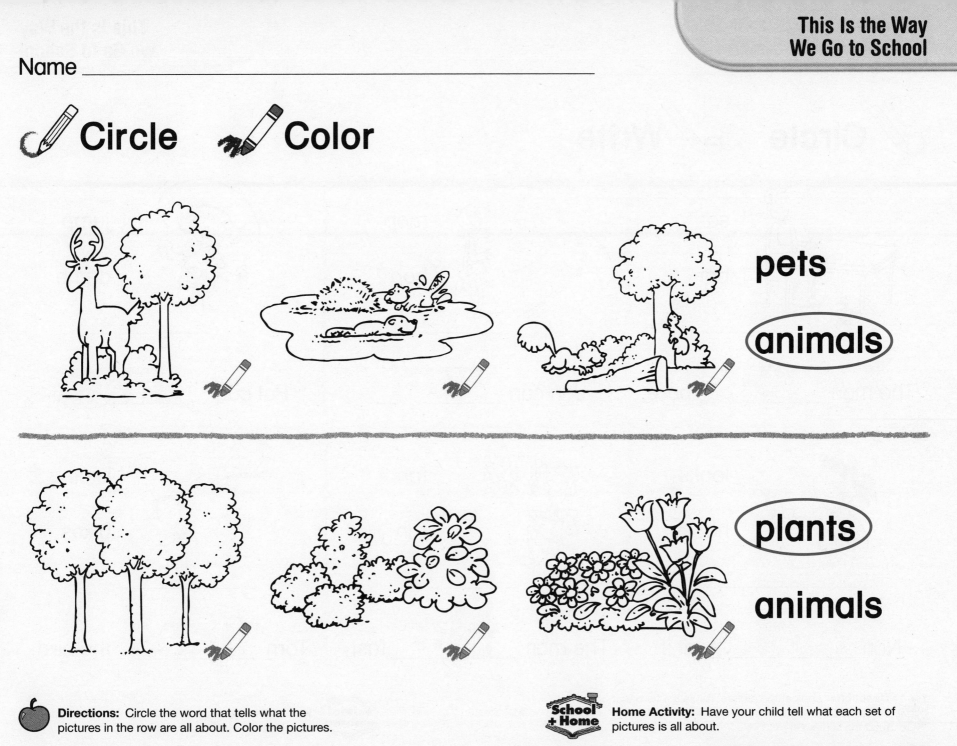

✏️ **Circle** 🖍️ **Color**

pets

(animals)

plants

animals

**Directions:** Circle the word that tells what the pictures in the row are all about. Color the pictures.

**Home Activity:** Have your child tell what each set of pictures is all about.

© Pearson Education, Inc., K

**Comprehension** Main Idea   **395**

Name _____

✏ Circle   ✏ Write

sat
bat

The man **sat** here.

mop
hop

Jan can **hop**.

jump
dump

Pat can **jump**.

looks
hooks

Nan **looks** at it.

fan
ran

The man **ran** fast.

likes
bikes

Tom **likes** the bird.

🍎 **Directions:** Look at the picture. Circle the verb that completes the sentence. Then write the word and read the sentence.

 **Home Activity:** Have your child use the verb that is not circled in each box in a sentence.

Name _____

 Write   Draw

I will add this to my draft.

_____

- - - - - - - - - - - - - - - - - - - - - - - - - - - -

_____

_____

- - - - - - - - - - - - - - - - - - - - - - - - - - - -

**Pictures and answers will vary.**

_____

**Directions** Have children draw pictures of and write or dictate additional details and sentences that could be included in the how-to report.

**School + Home**  **Home Activity** Have your child tell you how the class revised the how-to report to make it better.

Name _____

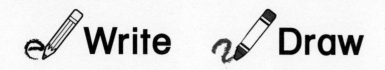 Write  Draw

_____

- - - - - - - - - - - - - - - - - - - - - - - - - - - - - - - - - - - - -

_____

- - - - - - - - - - - - - - - - - - - - - - - - - - - - - - - - - - - - -

_____

- - - - - - - - - - - - - - - - - - - - - - - - - - - - - - - - - - - - -

**Pictures and answers will vary.**

**Directions** Have children draw, write, or dictate the entire how-to report.

 **Home Activity** Discuss with your child another topic he or she would like to write about. Try drafting a how-to report on this topic.

Name _____

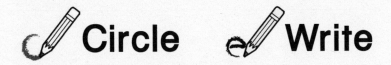 Circle    Write

1. how doyou do it

**How do you do it?**

2. first, sign up for a card

**First, sign up for a card.**

3. Last, show your newcard

**Last, show your new card.**

 **Directions** Have children circle the mistakes and rewrite the words or sentences correctly on the lines.

 **Home Activity** Have your child point out and explain his or her edits.

Name _____

✏️ Circle   ✏️ Write

I shared my selection with _____ **Answers will vary.** _____.

Here's what he/she learned.

_____

_____

_____

_____

**Directions** Have children circle the picture that shows with whom they shared their how-to report. Then have children ask the peer or adult reviewer to fill in the blanks and to discuss the how-to report with him or her.

**School + Home** **Home Activity** Ask your child to read or tell the how-to report to you.

Name _____

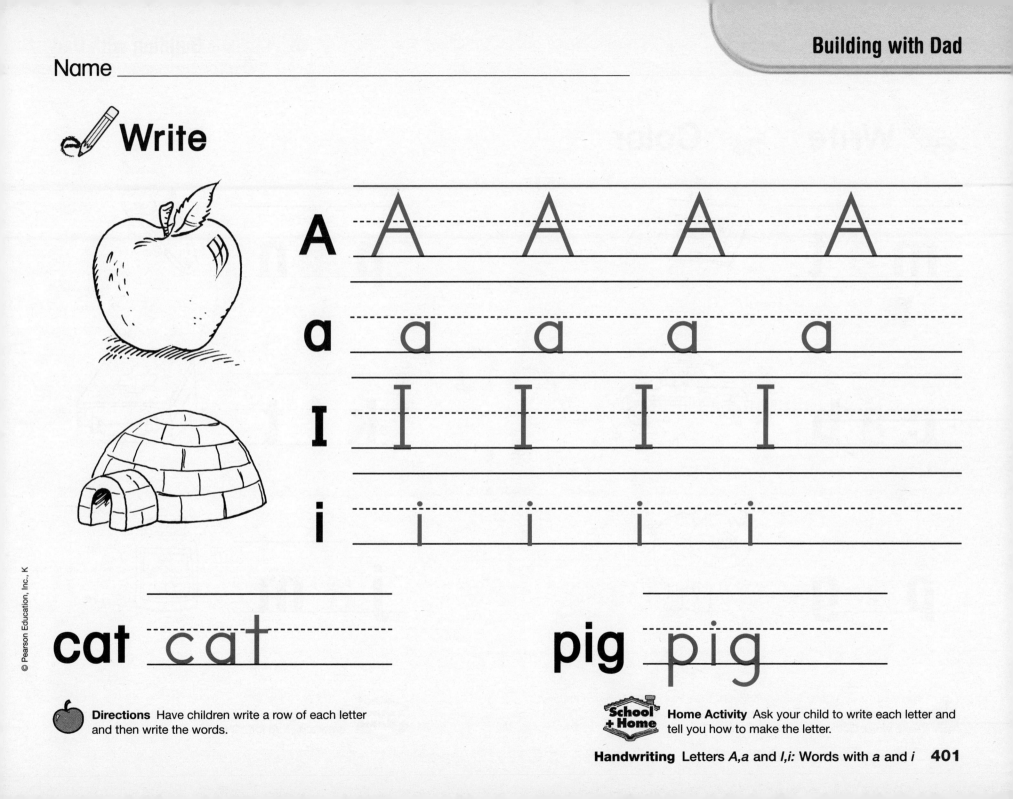

✎ **Write**

A   A   A   A   A

a   a   a   a   a

I   I   I   I   I

i   i   i   i   i

**cat** cat

**pig** pig

**Directions** Have children write a row of each letter and then write the words.

**School + Home** **Home Activity** Ask your child to write each letter and tell you how to make the letter.

Name _____

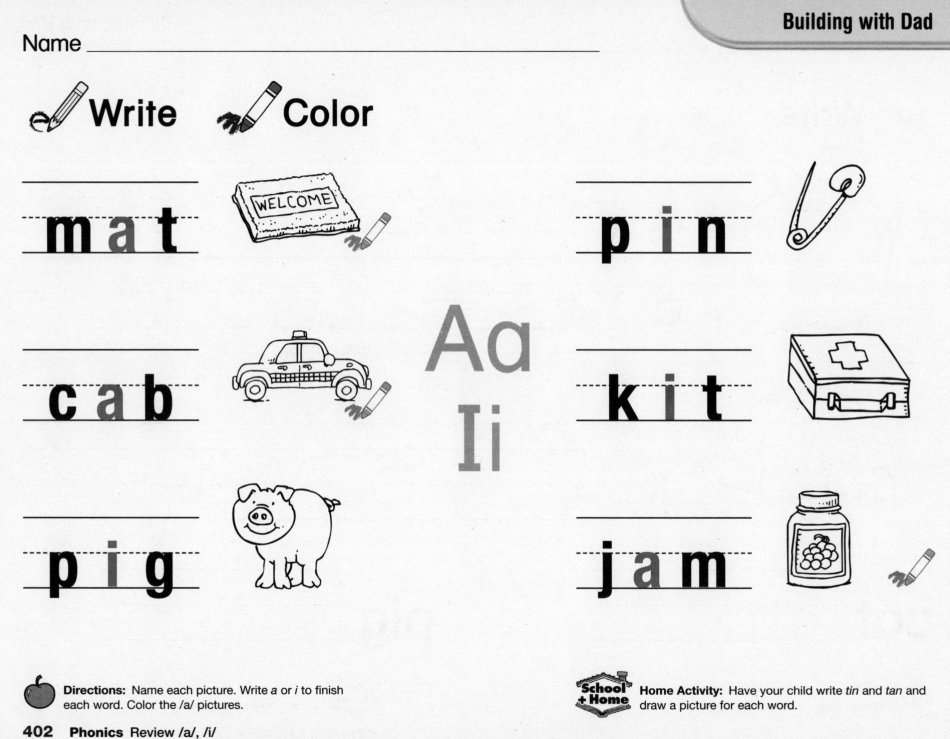

✏️ Write  🖍️ Color

m a t

c a b

p i g

Aa
Ii

p i n

k i t

j a m

**Directions:** Name each picture. Write *a* or *i* to finish each word. Color the /a/ pictures.

**Home Activity:** Have your child write *tin* and *tan* and draw a picture for each word.

Vin will zip the bag.

He and the bag will go on a trip.

4

# Vin and the Bag

Vin had a bag.

The bag is a big bag.

1

He got one big can.

He got one little net.

He got one little kit.

He got one big rag.

Name _____

✏️ **Write**    🖍️ **Color**

| what | with | do | little |

_____

**Do** ------------------- you like to jump?

_____

My dog is **little** .

_____

I will go **with** you.

_____

**What** can I do to help?

🍎 **Directions:** Write the missing word to finish each sentence. Color the pictures.

**School + Home**   **Home Activity:** Have your child use the high-frequency words in other sentences.

Name _____

 **Read It!**

I have a pet.

The pet is for me.

**Say It!**

Tell about something you have using the words **I** and **me.**

 **Write It!**

_____

– – – – **I** – – – – have a ball. (I)

_____

The ball is for _____ **me** _____ . (me)

 **Directions** Have children track the print and read the sentences about the pet. Ask them to say sentences for things they have using *I* and *me*. Then have children write the pronouns *I* and *me* to complete the sentences.

 **Home Activity** Have your child read the sentences and find the pronouns *I* and *me*. Then have him or her create other sentences with the pronouns *I* and *me*.

Name _____

✏️ Write 🖍️ Color

lid

fan

pin

hat

pig

six

© Pearson Education, Inc., K

**Directions:** Say the word that names the picture. Spell the picture name. Write the word on the lines. Color the /i/ pictures.

**School + Home**

**Home Activity:** Have your child draw a picture of something with /i/. Then help him or her spell and write the picture name.

Name ______________________________

## Color

**Directions:** Color the picture that is different in each row.

**School + Home** **Home Activity:** Have your child tell how the pictures are alike and how they are different.

Name _____

✏ Circle    ✏ Write

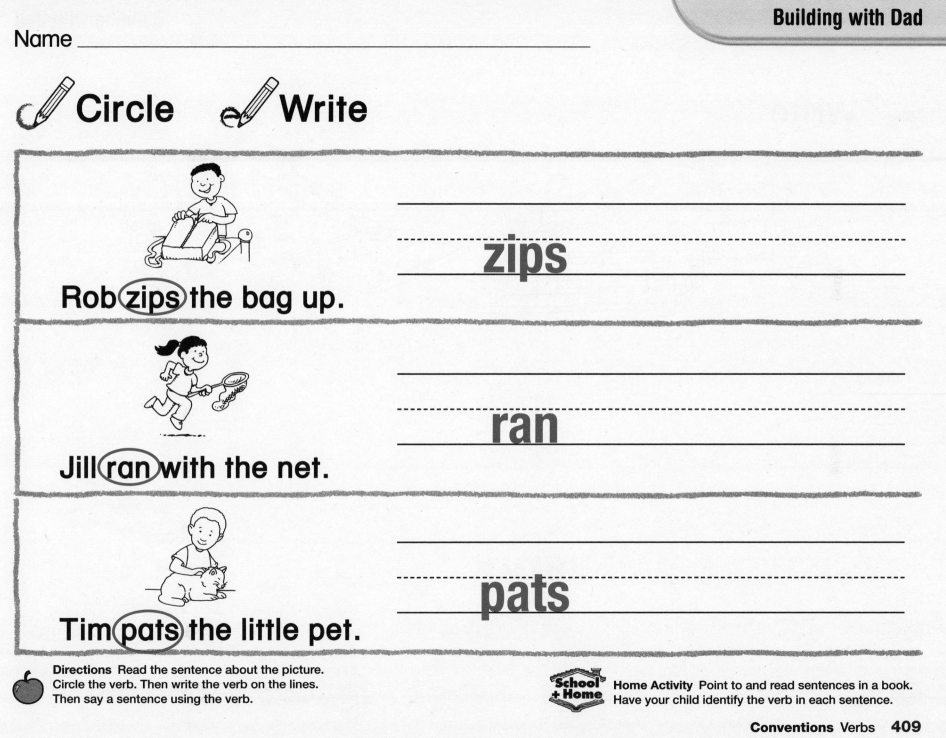

Rob zips the bag up.

zips

Jill ran with the net.

ran

Tim pats the little pet.

pats

**Directions** Read the sentence about the picture.
Circle the verb. Then write the verb on the lines.
Then say a sentence using the verb.

**School + Home** **Home Activity** Point to and read sentences in a book.
Have your child identify the verb in each sentence.

Name _____

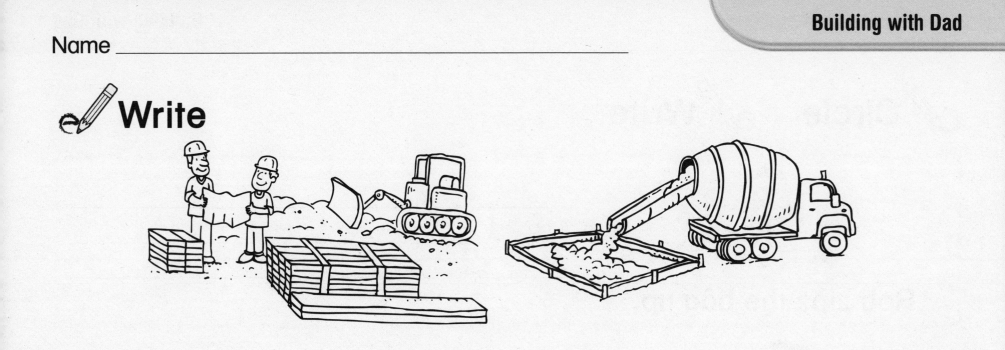

✏️ **Write**

# Answers will vary.

 **Directions** Write or dictate a list of things from *Building with Dad* that you want to learn more about.

 **School + Home** **Home Activity** Help your child write a list of toys he or she knows how to use.

Name _____

 Circle  Color

**Directions:** Circle the picture in the third box to tell what Carl eats. Color the pictures. Circle the picture in the third box to tell how Rosa gets to Australia. Color the pictures.

 **School + Home**

**Home Activity:** Have your child tell why he or she drew each conclusion.

Name _____

 **Read It!**

I have a book.

The book is for me.

**Say It!**

Tell about something you have using the words **I** and **me**.

 **Write It!**

_____

**I** have a hat. (I)

The hat is for ___ **me** ___ . (me)

 **Directions** Have children read the sentences about the book. Ask them to say sentences for things they have using *I* and *me*. Then have children write the pronouns *I* and *me* to complete the sentences.

 **Home Activity** Have your child create sentences with the pronouns *I* and *me*.

Name _____

✎ **Write**

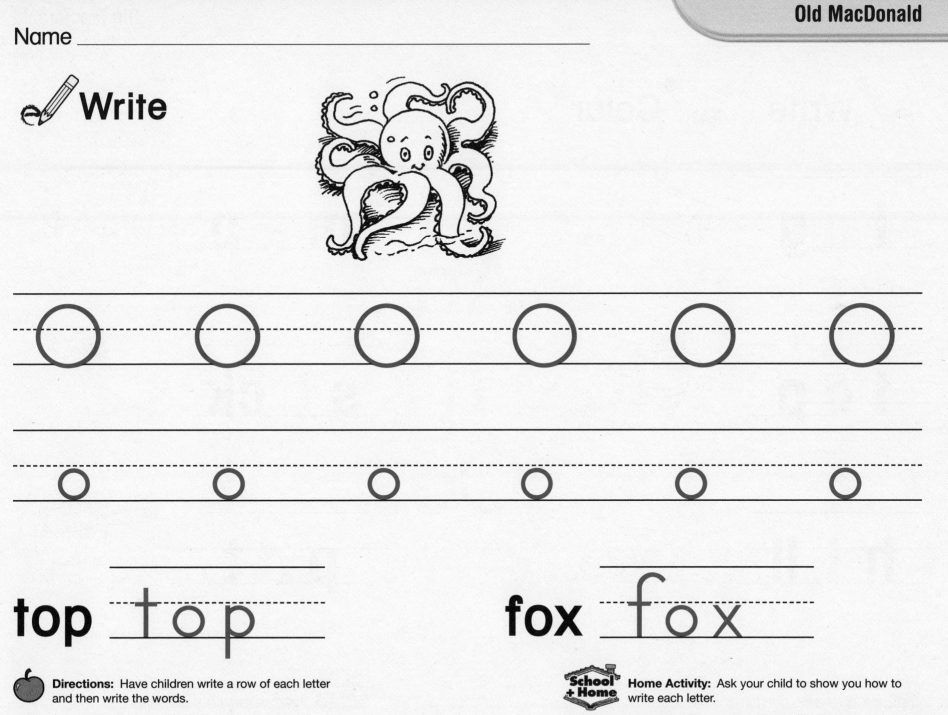

**top** <u>top</u>

**fox** <u>fox</u>

🍎 **Directions:** Have children write a row of each letter and then write the words.

**School + Home** **Home Activity:** Ask your child to show you how to write each letter.

Name _____

✏️ Write    🖍️ Color

l o g

t o p

h i l l

Aa
Ii
Oo

m a p

s o c k

p o t

🍎 **Directions:** Write *a, i,* or *o* to finish each word. Color the /o/ pictures.

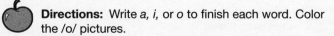

 **Home Activity:** Have your child write *lock* and *rock* and draw a picture for each word.

**414    Phonics** Review /a/, /i/, /o/

# Spin the Top

Dad will spin the top.

Dad can spin it.

Dad can get the top
to spin.

Bob got a top.

Bob will spin the top.

4

1

The top will not spin.

The top will not go.

Help! Help!

Help me spin the top.

It will not spin.

Help! Help!

Name _____

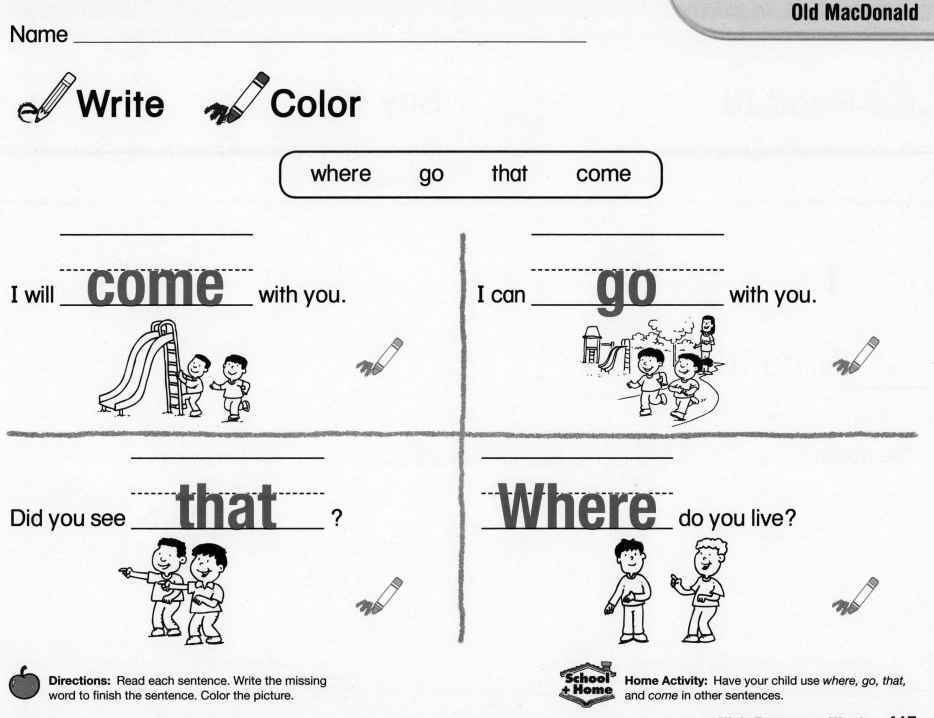

✏️ Write  🖍️ Color

| where | go | that | come |

_____
I will **come** with you.

_____
I can **go** with you.

_____
Did you see **that** ?

_____
**Where** do you live?

🍎 **Directions:** Read each sentence. Write the missing word to finish the sentence. Color the picture.

🏫 **School + Home** **Home Activity:** Have your child use *where, go, that,* and *come* in other sentences.

© Pearson Education, Inc., K

**High-Frequency Words** **417**

Name _____

 **Read It!**

The cat is on the box.

**Say It!**

Say a sentence about a dog using the phrase **in the box**.

 **Write It!**

The dog sat ____ **by the book** ____ (by the book).

**Directions** Have children track the print and read the sentence with you. Ask them to say a sentence with the phrase *in the box*. Have children write the prepositional phrase to complete the sentence.

**Home Activity** Have your child create sentences using the prepositional phrases *on the table, in the sink,* or *on the bed.*

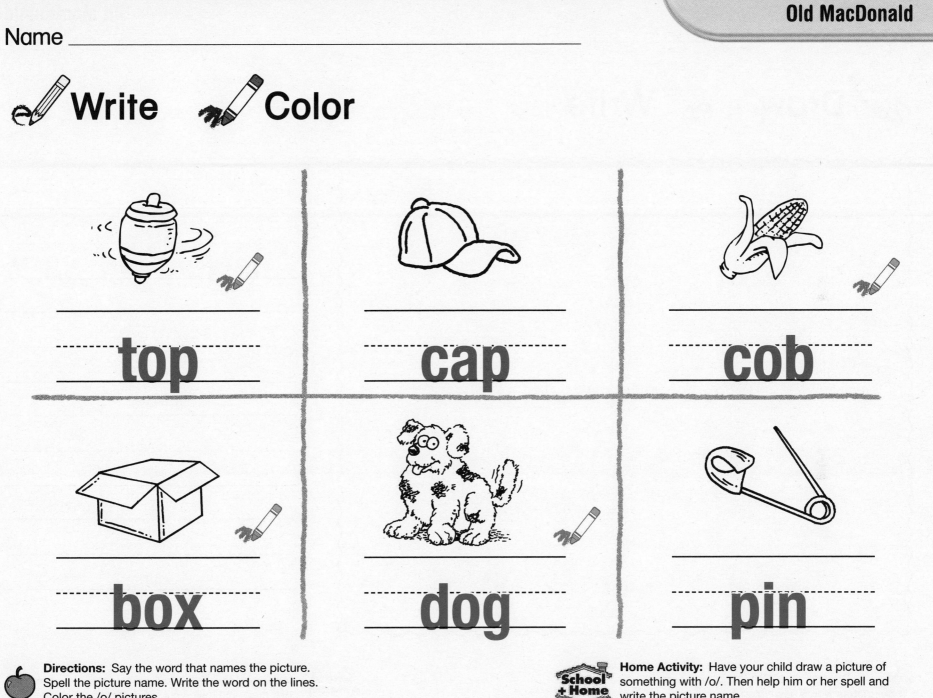

Name _____

✏️ **Write**   🖍️ **Color**

top

cap

cob

box

dog

pin

**Directions:** Say the word that names the picture. Spell the picture name. Write the word on the lines. Color the /o/ pictures.

**School + Home**

**Home Activity:** Have your child draw a picture of something with /o/. Then help him or her spell and write the picture name.

© Pearson Education, Inc., K

**Phonics** Review /a/, /i/, /o/   **419**

Name _____

✏️ **Draw**   ✏️ **Write**

**Answers will vary.**

**Directions:** Draw your favorite character from *Old MacDonald had a Woodshop*, and then write or dictate words describing it.

**Home Activity:** Talk about the favorite character your child drew and have your child describe it.

Name _____

 **Read It!**

I got a top.

The top is for me.

**Say It!**

Tell about something you have using the words **I** and **me**.

 **Write It!**

_____ **I** _____ have a toy car. (I)

The toy car is for _____ **me** _____. (me)

 **Directions** Have children track the print and read the sentences with you. Ask them to say sentences for things they have using *I* and *me*. Then have children write the pronouns *I* and *me* to complete the sentences.

 **Home Activity** Have your child read the sentences and find the pronouns *I* and *me*. Then have him or her create other sentences with the pronouns *I* and *me*.

**Conventions** Pronouns *I* and *Me*  **421**

Name _____

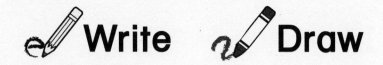 Write  Draw

## Old MacDonald had a farm, E-I-E-I-O.

_____

And on his farm he had a _____

Answers will vary.

 **Directions** Have children complete the song about Old MacDonald by writing or dictating a kind of animal. Then have each child draw a picture of the animal he or she chose.

 **Home Activity** Help your child create another verse for the "Old MacDonald Had a Farm" song.

Name _____

# ✎ Draw

draw man and boy riding bikes

draw girl eating cereal

**Directions:** Draw a picture to show what would happen next in each story.

**School + Home**

**Home Activity:** With your child, retell a familiar story. You begin the story and ask your child to tell what happens next.

**Comprehension** Plot  **423**

Name _____

 **Read It!**

The bug is in the tub.

**Say It!**

Say a sentence using the phrase **on the window.**

 **Write It!**

_____

The bug ran _____**on the rug**_____ (on the rug).

 **Directions** Have children track the print and read the sentence with you. Ask them to use the phrase *on the window* in a sentence. Then have children write the prepositional phrase *on the rug* to complete the sentence.

 **Home Activity** Have your child create sentences using the prepositional phrases *on the chair, in the book,* or *under the couch.*

Name _____

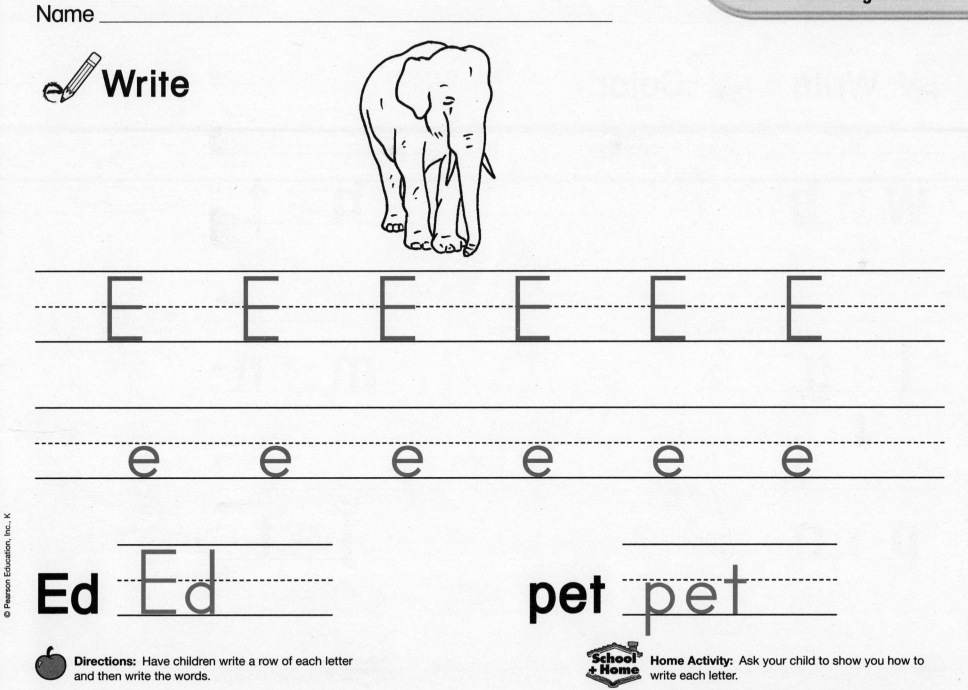

## ✏️ Write

E E E E E

e e e e e e

**Ed** Ed

**pet** pet

**Directions:** Have children write a row of each letter and then write the words.

**Home Activity:** Ask your child to show you how to write each letter.

Name _____

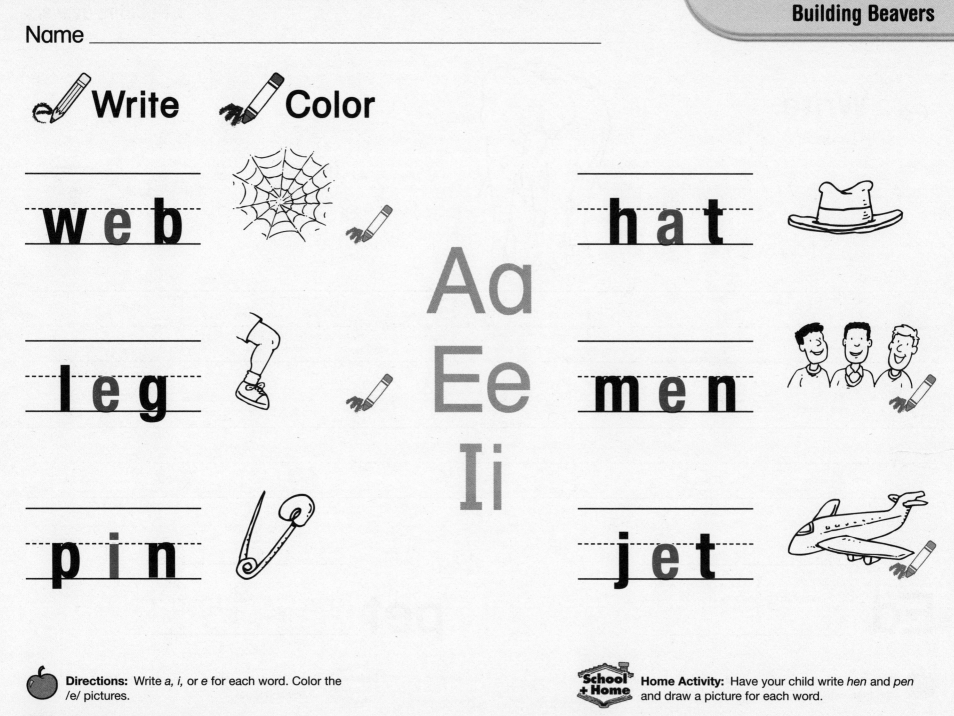

✏️ Write   🖍️ Color

w e b

l e g

p i n

Aa
Ee
Ii

h a t

m e n

j e t

**Directions:** Write *a, i,* or *e* for each word. Color the /e/ pictures.

**Home Activity:** Have your child write *hen* and *pen* and draw a picture for each word.

The hen had little ones.

Jim and Kim have lots of little hens.

**Decodable Story** *Jim and Kim*
**Target Skill** Review

---

# Jim and Kim

Jim and Kim had a pet.

They had a pet hen.

The hen was in a pen.

Jim had fun with the pet hen.

Jim fed the hen.

Kim had fun with the pet hen.

Kim got a nest for the hen.

Name _____

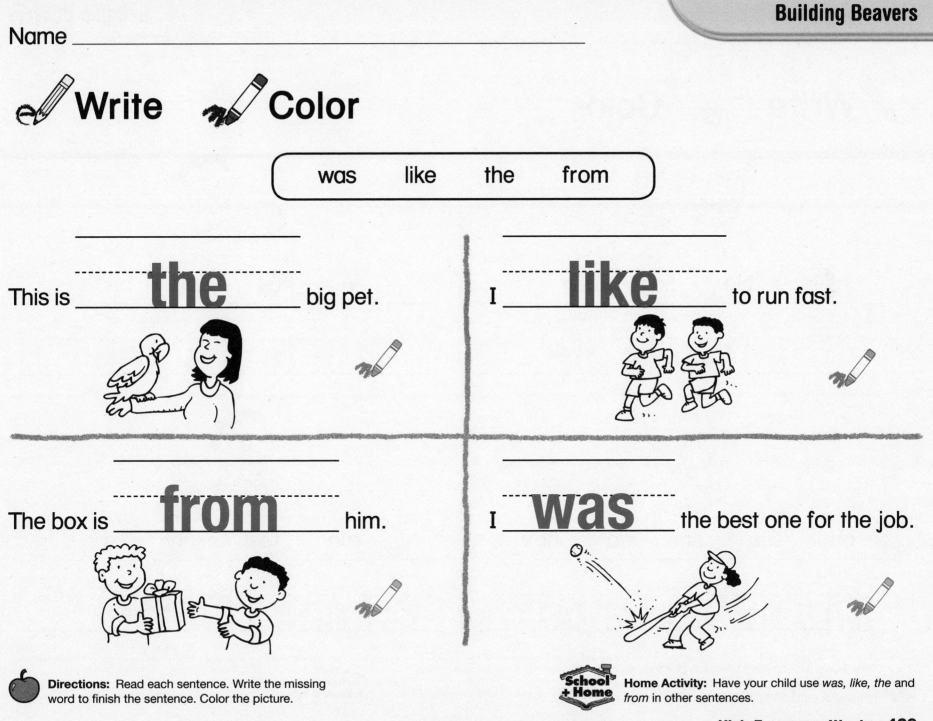

✏️ **Write**     🖍️ **Color**

was     like     the     from

_____

This is __**the**__ big pet.

_____

I __**like**__ to run fast.

_____

The box is __**from**__ him.

_____

I __**was**__ the best one for the job.

🍎 **Directions:** Read each sentence. Write the missing word to finish the sentence. Color the picture.

**School + Home**  **Home Activity:** Have your child use *was, like, the* and *from* in other sentences.

Name _____

✏️ Write   🖍️ Color

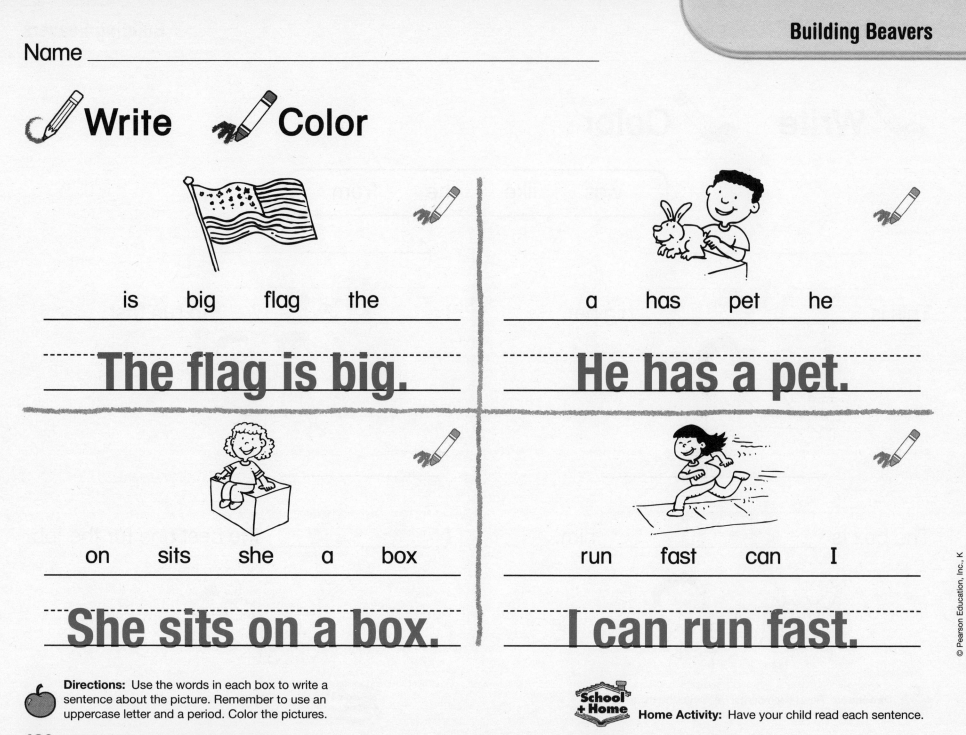

is   big   flag   the

**The flag is big.**

a   has   pet   he

**He has a pet.**

on   sits   she   a   box

**She sits on a box.**

run   fast   can   I

**I can run fast.**

**Directions:** Use the words in each box to write a sentence about the picture. Remember to use an uppercase letter and a period. Color the pictures.

**School + Home**

**Home Activity:** Have your child read each sentence.

Name _____

 Write  Color

net

bed

10

ten

pot

hen

cat

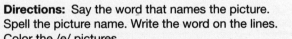

**Directions:** Say the word that names the picture. Spell the picture name. Write the word on the lines. Color the /e/ pictures.

**Home Activity:** Have your child draw a picture of something with /e/. Then help him or her spell and write the picture name.

School + Home

Name _____

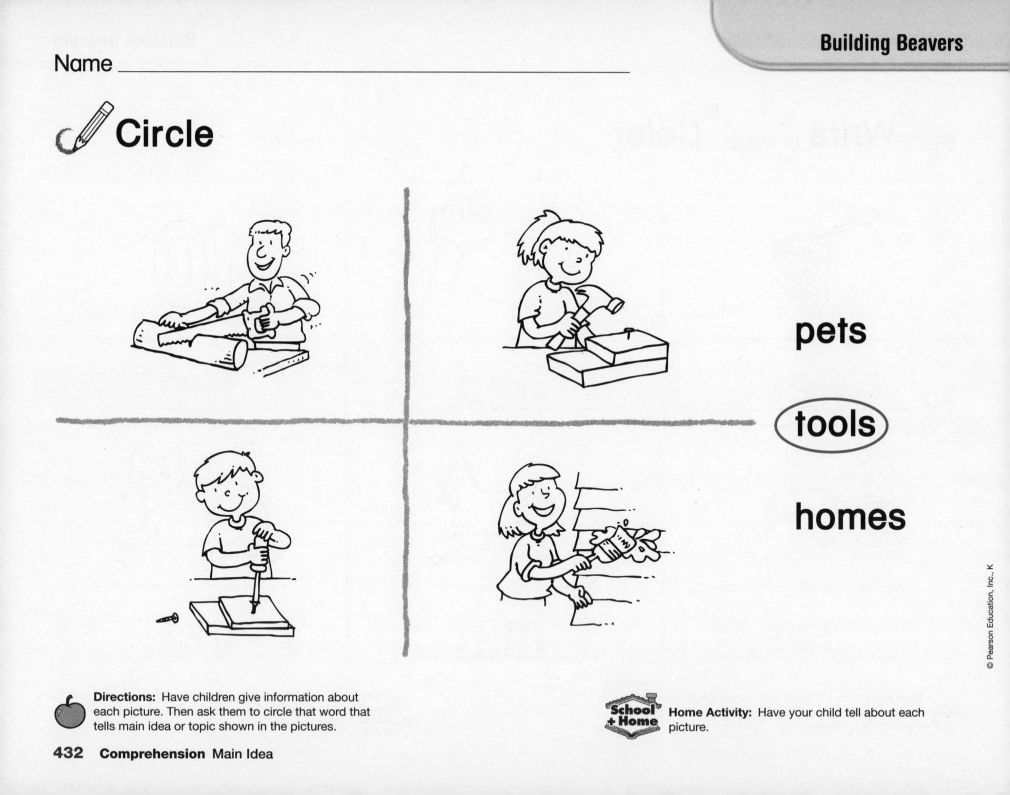

✏️ Circle

pets

(tools)

homes

**Directions:** Have children give information about each picture. Then ask them to circle that word that tells main idea or topic shown in the pictures.

**School + Home**

**Home Activity:** Have your child tell about each picture.

**432** **Comprehension** Main Idea

© Pearson Education, Inc., K

Name _____

 **Read It!**

The hen is in the pen.

**Say It!**

Say a sentence about an animal using the phrase **under the tree.**

 **Write It!**

The duck is _____ **on the leaf** _____ (on the leaf).

**Directions** Have children track the print and read the sentence with you. Ask them to say a sentence with the phrase *under the tree.* Then have children write the prepositional phrase to complete the sentence.

**School + Home**

**Home Activity** Have your child create sentences using the prepositional phrases *on the table* and *in the sink.*

Name _____

 **Write**   **Draw**

---
- - - - - - - - - - - - - - - - - - - - - -
---
---
- - - - - - - - - - - - - - - - - - - - - -
---

**Answers will vary.**

 **Directions** Have children copy the rhyme they created about the beavers. Then have them draw a picture of the beaver.

 **Home Activity** Help your child make a rhyme about an animal and draw the animal's picture.

Name _____

✏️ **Draw** 🖍️ **Color**

**Directions:** Draw a line from what happened to why it happened. Color each picture.

 **Home Activity:** Have your child tell you what happened in each picture in the first row and why it happened.

**Comprehension** Cause and Effect  **435**

Name _____

✏️ Write 🖍️ Color

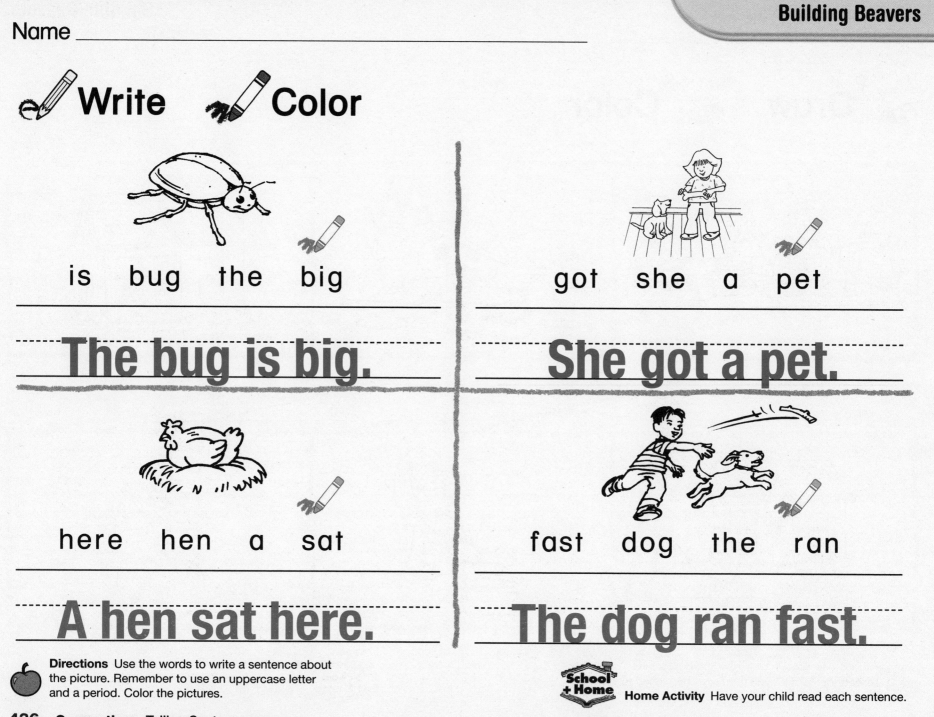

is    bug    the    big

**The bug is big.**

got    she    a    pet

**She got a pet.**

here    hen    a    sat

**A hen sat here.**

fast    dog    the    ran

**The dog ran fast.**

**Directions** Use the words to write a sentence about the picture. Remember to use an uppercase letter and a period. Color the pictures.

**School + Home**

**Home Activity** Have your child read each sentence.

Name _____

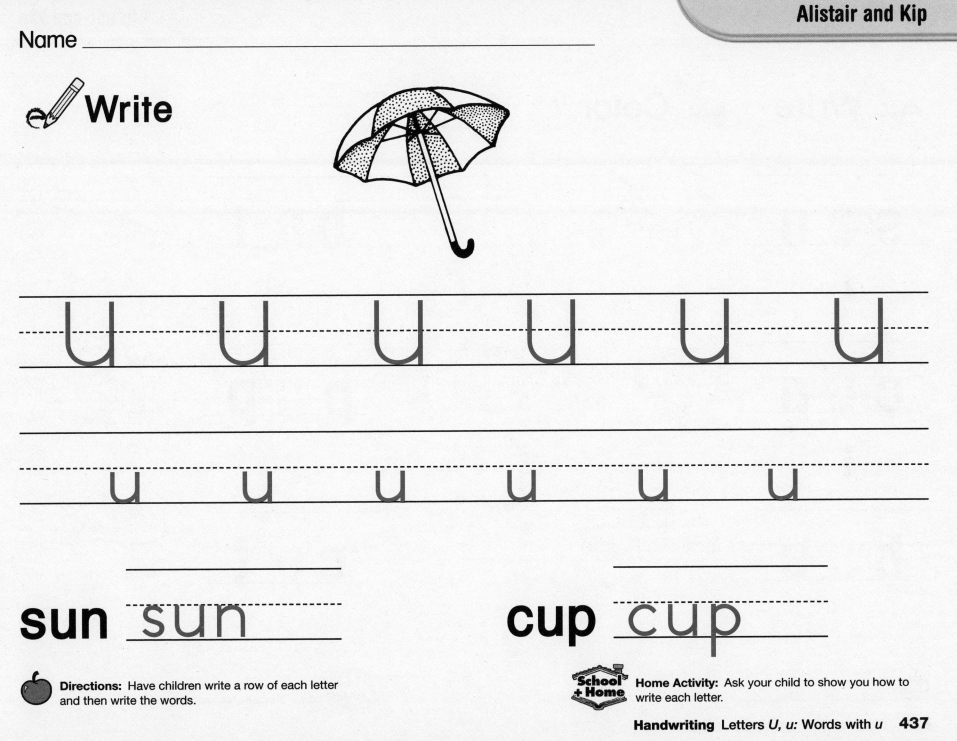

✎ Write

u  u  u  u  u  u  u

u  u  u  u  u  u

**sun** sun

**cup** cup

🍎 **Directions:** Have children write a row of each letter and then write the words.

🏫 School + Home  **Home Activity:** Ask your child to show you how to write each letter.

**Handwriting** Letters *U, u:* Words with *u*  **437**

Name _____

✏️ Write   🖍️ Color

sun

cup

bus

Aa
Oo
Uu

bat

pup

cot

 **Directions:** Write *a*, *o*, or *u* to finish each word.
Color the /u/ pictures.

 **Home Activity:** Have your child write *hut* and *nut* and
draw a picture for each word.

Gus grabs the bug.

Gus lets the bug go.

4

# Gus and the Bug

Gus will hug his mom.

Gus gets on the bus.

1

Gus sat with his pal Wes.

The sun was hot.

A bug got on the bus.

It sat with Gus and Wes.

Name _____

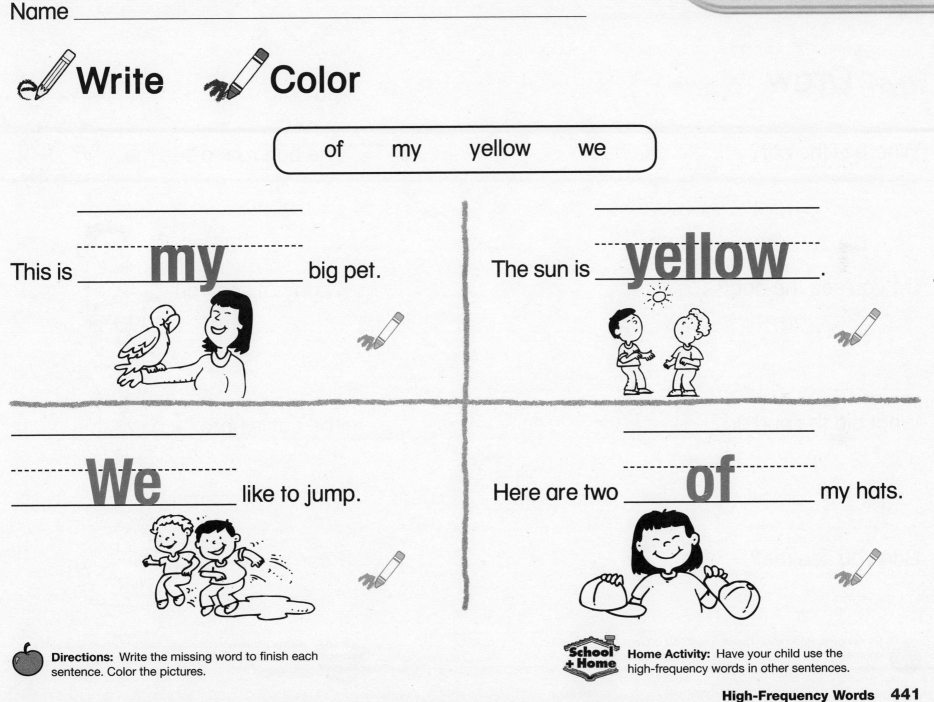

**Write**    **Color**

of    my    yellow    we

This is _____**my**_____ big pet.

The sun is ____**yellow**____ .

____**We**____ like to jump.

Here are two ____**of**____ my hats.

**Directions:** Write the missing word to finish each sentence. Color the pictures.

**School + Home**

**Home Activity:** Have your child use the high-frequency words in other sentences.

Name _____

# ✏️ Draw

Where is the cat?                    The bug ran to see me.

Do you see the dog?                    I can not see you.

What did the bug do?                    The cat is here.

Can you see me?                    I can see the dog.

**Directions:** Read each question and the answer choices aloud. Then draw a line from each question to its answer.

**Home Activity:** Ask your child the questions and have him or her create an answer using a complete sentence.

School + Home

Name _____

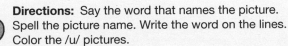 Write  Color

_____

nut

_____

cat

_____

cub

_____

log

_____

rug

_____

ten

**Directions:** Say the word that names the picture. Spell the picture name. Write the word on the lines. Color the /u/ pictures.

**School + Home**

**Home Activity:** Have your child draw a picture of something with /u/. Then help him or her spell and write the picture name.

Name _____

 Color

**Directions:** Color the picture that shows what would happen next in each story.

 **Home Activity:** Have your child tell you the story of *Alistair and Kip's Great Adventure*.

**444** **Comprehension** Plot

Name _____

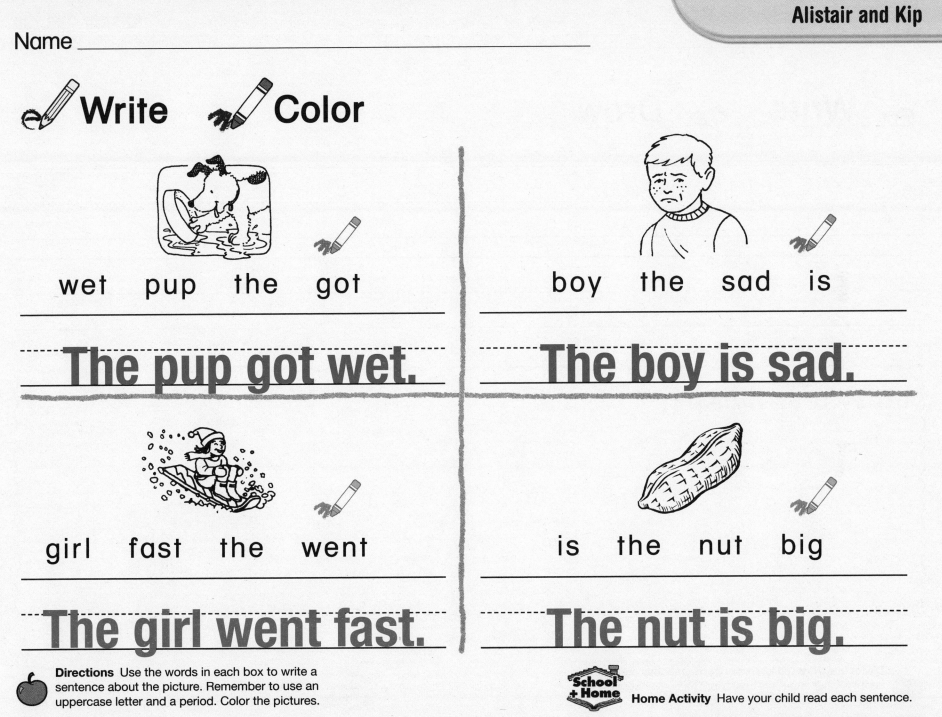

✏️ **Write**   🖍️ **Color**

wet   pup   the   got

_____

**The pup got wet.**

boy   the   sad   is

_____

**The boy is sad.**

girl   fast   the   went

_____

**The girl went fast.**

is   the   nut   big

_____

**The nut is big.**

© Pearson Education, Inc., K

**Directions** Use the words in each box to write a sentence about the picture. Remember to use an uppercase letter and a period. Color the pictures.

**School + Home**   **Home Activity** Have your child read each sentence.

Name _____

 Write  Draw

_____

- - - - - - - - - - - - - - - - - - - - - -

_____

_____

- - - - - - - - - - - - - - - - - - - - - -

_____

Answers will vary.

**Directions** Have children say the rhyme they created about Alistair and Kip's boat trip. Then have them write the rhyme and draw a picture of the trip.

 **School + Home** **Home Activity** Help your child make a rhyme about a trip and draw a picture to tell more about the trip.

Name _____

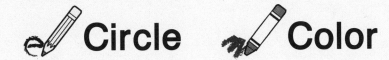 Circle ✏️ Color

 **Directions:** Circle the picture in the top right box to tell how Ann gets to school. Color the pictures. Circle the picture in the bottom right box to tell which kitten Joe gets. Color the pictures.

 **School + Home** **Home Activity:** Have your child tell why he or she drew each conclusion.

**Comprehension** Draw Conclusions **447**

© Pearson Education, Inc., K

Name _____

# ✏️ Draw

Where is the pup?                I can see the bus. 🚌

Can you see the bus?             The hen is not little. 🐔

What can the cat do?             The pup is here. 🐶

Is the hen little?               The cat can run. 🐱

🍎 **Directions** Read each question and the answer choices aloud. Then draw a line from each question to its answer.

🏠 **School + Home** **Home Activity** Use these question frames and add a household item: *Is the ___ big? Where is the ___?* Ask your child to repeat the question and give an answer. Then have your child create questions for you to answer.

Name _____

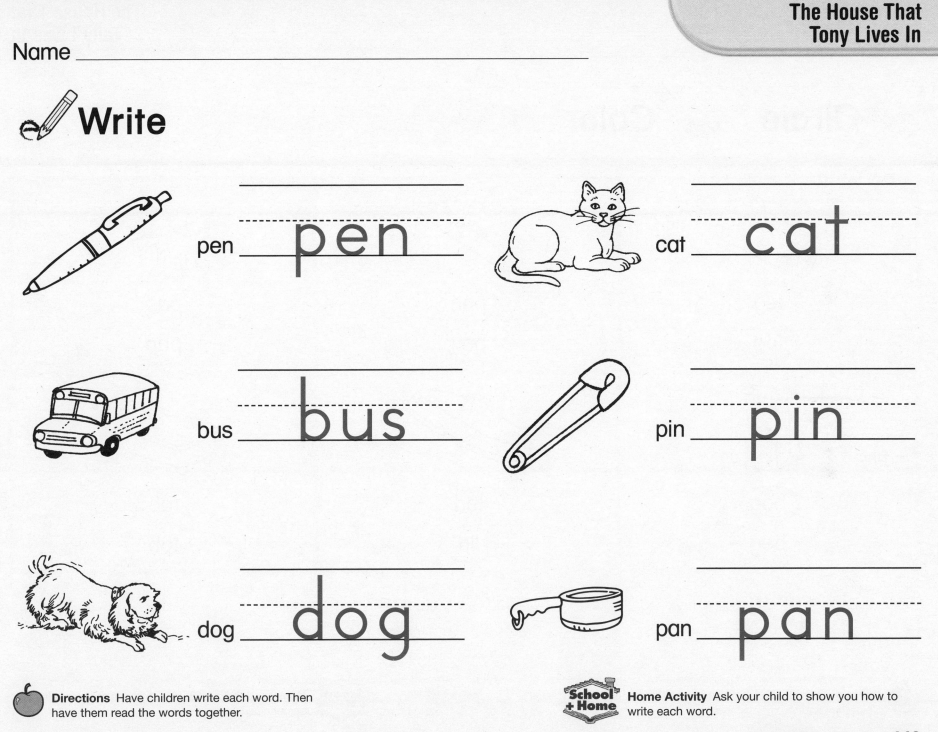

## ✏️ Write

pen ___ **pen** ___

cat ___ **cat** ___

bus ___ **bus** ___

pin ___ **pin** ___

dog ___ **dog** ___

pan ___ **pan** ___

🍎 **Directions** Have children write each word. Then have them read the words together.

**School + Home** **Home Activity** Ask your child to show you how to write each word.

Name _____

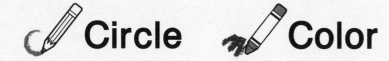 Circle  Color

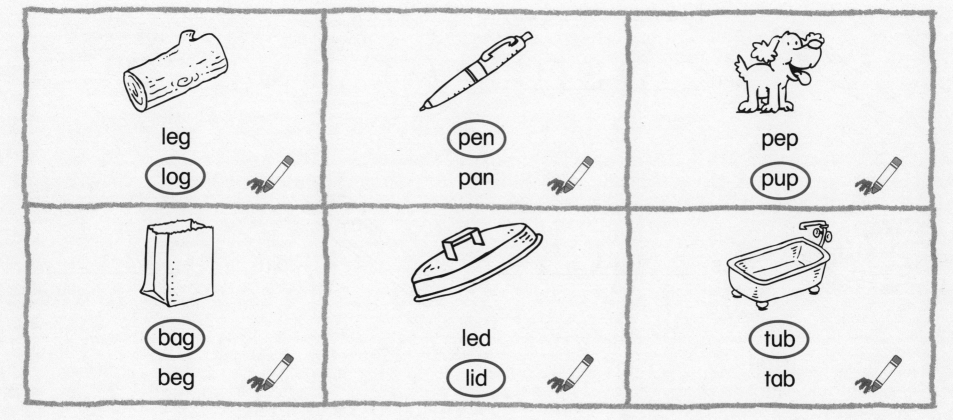

leg
(log)

(pen)
pan

pep
(pup)

(bag)
beg

led
(lid)

(tub)
tab

**Directions:** Circle the word that names the picture.
Color the pictures.

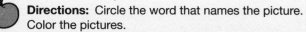

 **Home Activity:** Have your child use the words in sentences.

**450** **Phonics** Review /a/, /e/, /i/, /o/, /u/

Sam is a cat.

Sam will sit in a lap.

He will nap.

4

**Decodable Story** *What Pets Do*
**Target Skill** Review

# What Pets Do

Peg is a dog.

She will tug.

She will dig.

1

Hal is a pet pig.

He will run in his pen.

He will go in the mud.

Tad is a pet frog.

He will hop.

He will swim.

Name _____

✏️ **Write**   🖍️ **Color**

| blue | they | have | four |
|------|------|------|------|

_____

Do I still look ____**four**____ ?

_____

The bed is ____**blue**____ .

_____

We can ____**have**____ fun.

_____

____**They**____ play with a ball.

**Directions:** Read each sentence. Write the missing word to finish the sentence. Color the picture.

**School + Home**  **Home Activity:** Have your child use the high-frequency words in other sentences.

**High-Frequency Words**   **453**

© Pearson Education, Inc., K

Name _____

 Circle    ✎ Write

Can I swim _____

(Yes, I can)  ⌐⌐⌐ **Yes, I can!** ⌐⌐⌐

(I am glad)  _____

Is the pig big  ⌐⌐⌐ **I am glad!** ⌐⌐⌐

Is he sad  _____

(Help me)  ⌐⌐⌐ **Help me!** ⌐⌐⌐

🍎 **Directions** Circle the sentence that is an exclamation. Write the sentence. Use an exclamation mark.

**School + Home** **Home Activity** Have your child read each exclamation and point to the exclamation mark.

Name _____

 Write  Color

_____

fan

_____

cab

_____

man

_____

bed

_____

pan

_____

can

© Pearson Education, Inc., K

**Directions:** Name each picture and spell the picture name.
Write the word on the lines. Then color the pictures that rhyme.

 **Home Activity:** Have your child use the picture
names in sentences.

Name _____

**Color**

**Directions:** Color the picture that shows the setting of the story *The House That Tony Lives In*.

**Home Activity:** Have your child tell you when and where the story takes place.

School + Home

Name _____

# ✏️ Draw

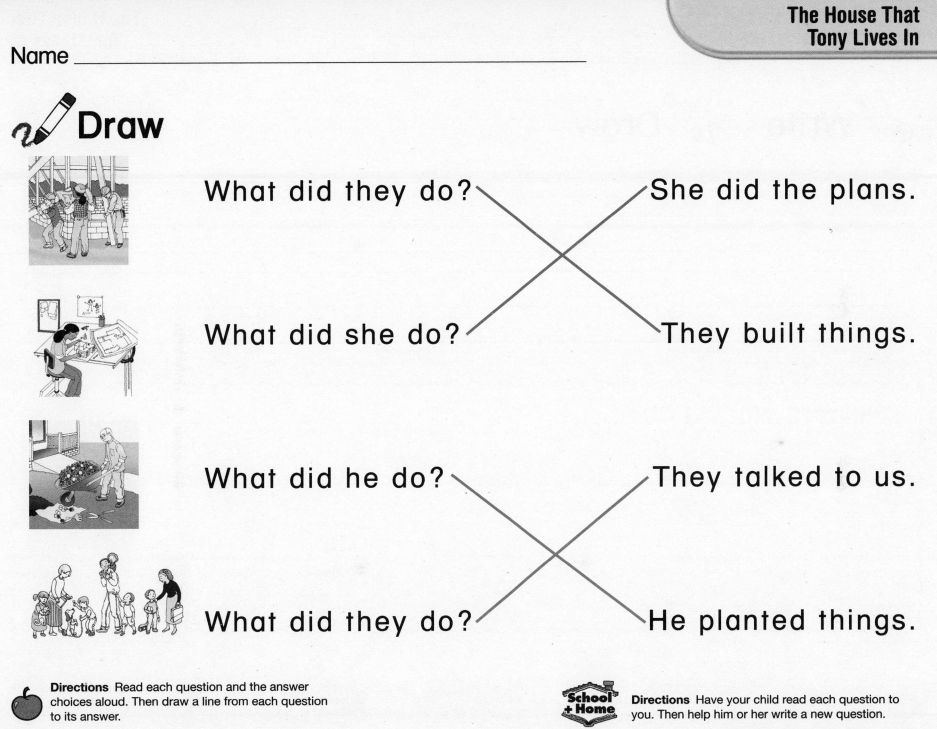

What did they do?

She did the plans.

What did she do?

They built things.

What did he do?

They talked to us.

What did they do?

He planted things.

**Directions** Read each question and the answer choices aloud. Then draw a line from each question to its answer.

**School + Home**

**Directions** Have your child read each question to you. Then help him or her write a new question.

© Pearson Education, Inc., K

Name _____

✏️ Write   🖍 Draw

_____
------------------------------------------------
_____
_____
------------------------------------------------
_____

Answers will vary.

🍎 **Directions** Have children copy the poem about a house. Then have them draw a picture of the house.

**Home Activity** Help your child make a poem with rhyming words such as *rug, bug, tug, dug, hug, jug,* and *mug*.

458 **Writing** Poem

Name _____

 Circle  Color

 **Directions:** Circle the make-believe pictures. Color the real pictures.

 **Home Activity:** With your child, look at a book about how real animals live.

**Comprehension** Realism and Fantasy  **459**

Name _____

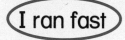 **Circle**     **Write**

Can you run fast

(I ran fast)

## I ran fast!

(I like it)

Will I get a pet

## I like it!

So you like my pet

(That was fun)

## That was fun!

 **Directions** Circle the sentence that is an exclamation.
Write the sentence. Use an exclamation mark.

**460** **Conventions** Exclamations

 **Home Activity** Have your child read each exclamation
and point to the exclamation mark.

Name _____

✏️ **Write**

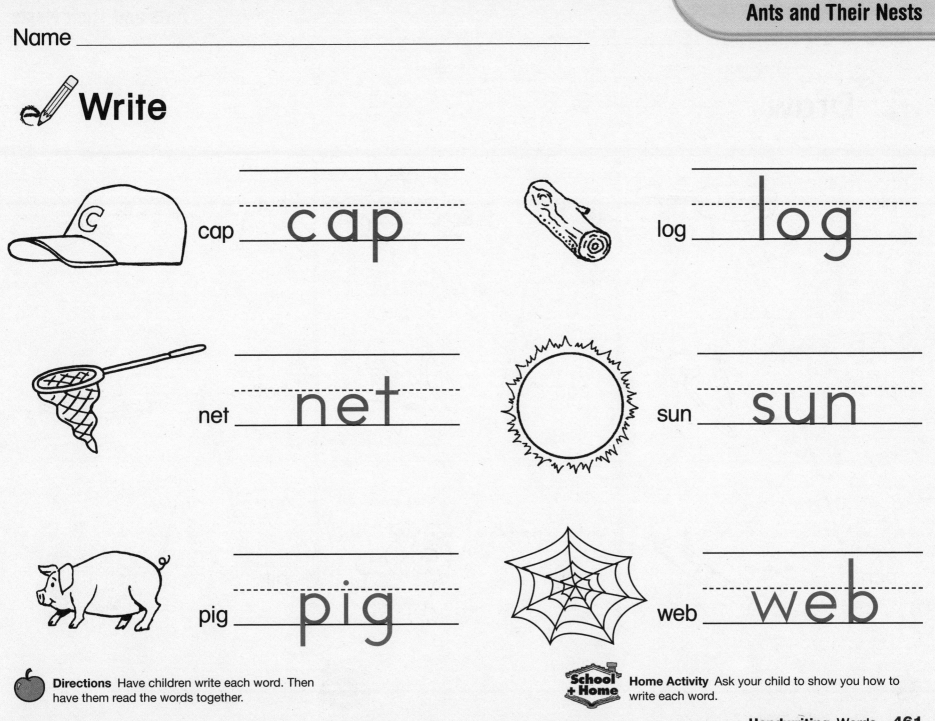

cap    cap

log    log

net    net

sun    sun

pig    pig

web    web

🍎 **Directions** Have children write each word. Then have them read the words together.

🏫 **School + Home** **Home Activity** Ask your child to show you how to write each word.

Name _____

# ✏️ Draw

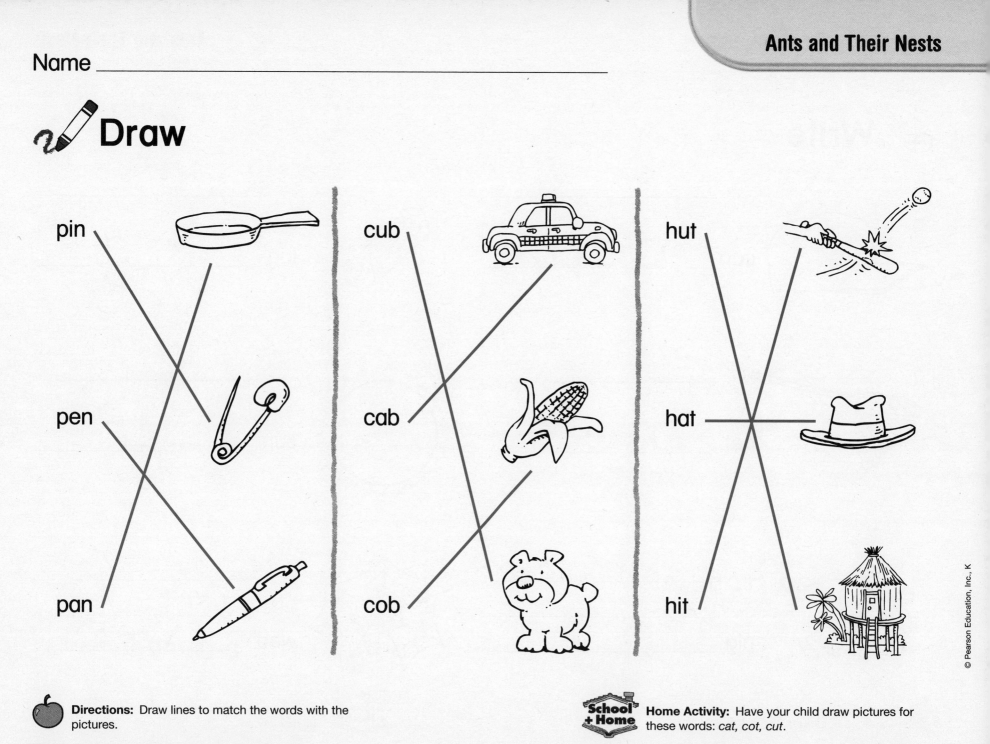

pin

pen

pan

cub

cab

cob

hut

hat

hit

**Directions:** Draw lines to match the words with the pictures.

**School + Home**

**Home Activity:** Have your child draw pictures for these words: *cat, cot, cut*.

I am Jen.

I can hang from my legs.

What can you do?

**Decodable Story** *What Can You Do?*
**Target Skill** Review

# What Can You Do?

Here is Ned.

Ned can run fast.

Ned can run and run.

Look at Ken.

He fed the big dog.

He fed the little dogs.

See Kim jump.

She can go from me to you.

She can jump from here
to here.

Name _____

 **Draw**

# Pictures will vary.

**Directions** Have children draw pictures of animals as report topic ideas.

 **Home Activity** Ask your child to tell you about his or her pictures of topic ideas.

Name _____

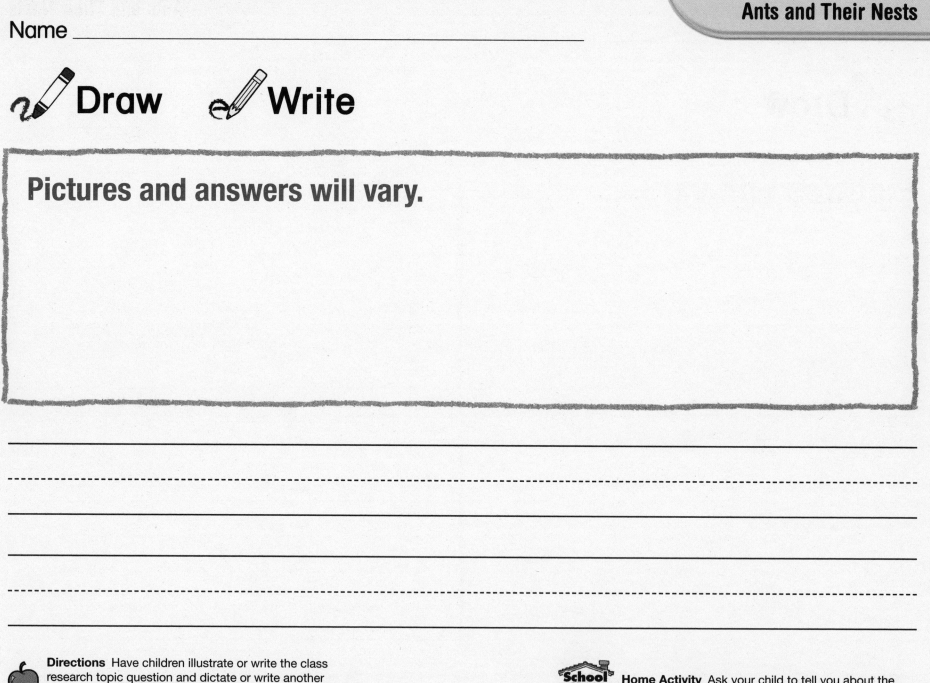

✏️ Draw  ✏️ Write

> Pictures and answers will vary.

----------------------------------------

- - - - - - - - - - - - - - - - - - - - -

----------------------------------------

- - - - - - - - - - - - - - - - - - - - -

----------------------------------------

© Pearson Education, Inc., K

🍎 **Directions** Have children illustrate or write the class research topic question and dictate or write another question about the topic.

**Home Activity** Ask your child to tell you about the report the class is planning to write.

Name _____

✏️ Write    🖍️ Color

| three | said | look | you |

_____
**Look** at that bug.

I **said** I will run fast.

Do **you** like hot dogs?

I have **three** cats.

🍎 **Directions:** Read each sentence. Write the missing word to finish the sentence. Color the picture.

🏫 **School + Home** **Home Activity:** Have your child use the high-frequency words in other sentences.

Name _____

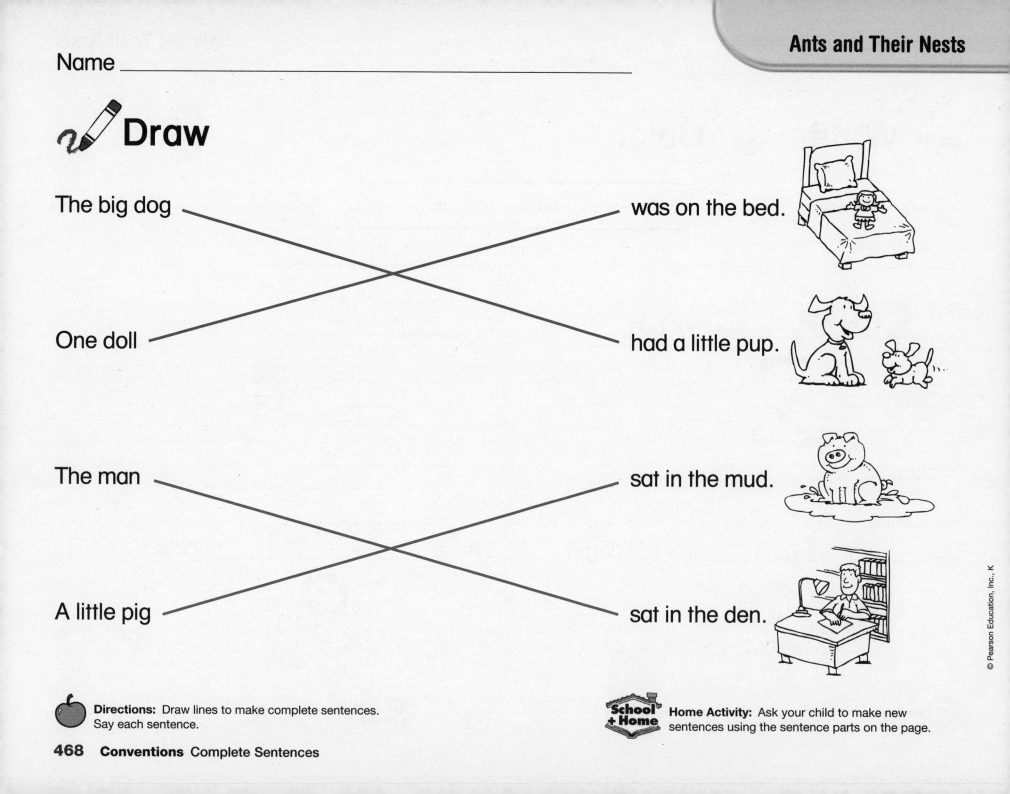

## ✏️ Draw

The big dog — was on the bed.

One doll — had a little pup.

The man — sat in the mud.

A little pig — sat in the den.

**Directions:** Draw lines to make complete sentences.
Say each sentence.

**Home Activity:** Ask your child to make new
sentences using the sentence parts on the page.

Name _____

 **Circle**

**Answers will vary.**

Hundreds attend parade

**Newspaper**

**Computer**

**Librarian**

**Television**

 **Directions** Ask: Which sources would you use to find out about animal homes? Have children circle the best source(s) for that information and then tell why.

**School + Home** **Home Activity** Discuss with your child ways that a newspaper can be a good source of information.

Name _____

 Circle  Draw

## Answers will vary.

**Computer**

**Book**

**Radio**

**Directions** Ask: Which sources would you use to find out what rabbits eat? Have children circle the best source(s) for that information. In the empty space, have them draw another source they could use to answer the question. Discuss their choices.

**Home Activity** Suggest various types of information and have your child tell where to look for the information.

School + Home

© Pearson Education, Inc., K

Name _____

# ✏ Write

cat

cot

bag

bug

pin

pan

net

nut

**Directions:** Name each picture and spell the picture name. Write the word on the lines.

**School + Home**

**Home Activity:** Have your child write *mop* and *map* and draw a picture for each word.

**Phonics** Review /a/, /e/, /i/, /o/, /u/  **471**

Name _____

# ✏️ Circle

**Directions:** Look at the animal home. Which animal would live in this home? Circle the animal.

🏠 **School + Home** **Home Activity:** Have your child explain how he or she arrived at each conclusion.

**472 Comprehension** Draw Conclusions

Name _____

✏️ **Write**

what a big bug

**What a big bug!**

we went fast

**We went fast!**

we win

**We win!**

🍎 **Directions** Read the words. Write the words to make an exclamation. Remember to use an exclamation mark at the end of the sentence.

**School + Home**

**Home Activity** Help your child write other exclamations.

Name _____

✏️ Write    🖍️ Draw

_____

1. _____

2. _____

3. _____

**Answers will vary.**

**Directions** Have children write, dictate, or copy their draft or key words from the class report. Draw pictures for the words in your list.

**School + Home**

**Home Activity** Ask your child to tell you what he or she learned about the topic of the class report.

Name _____

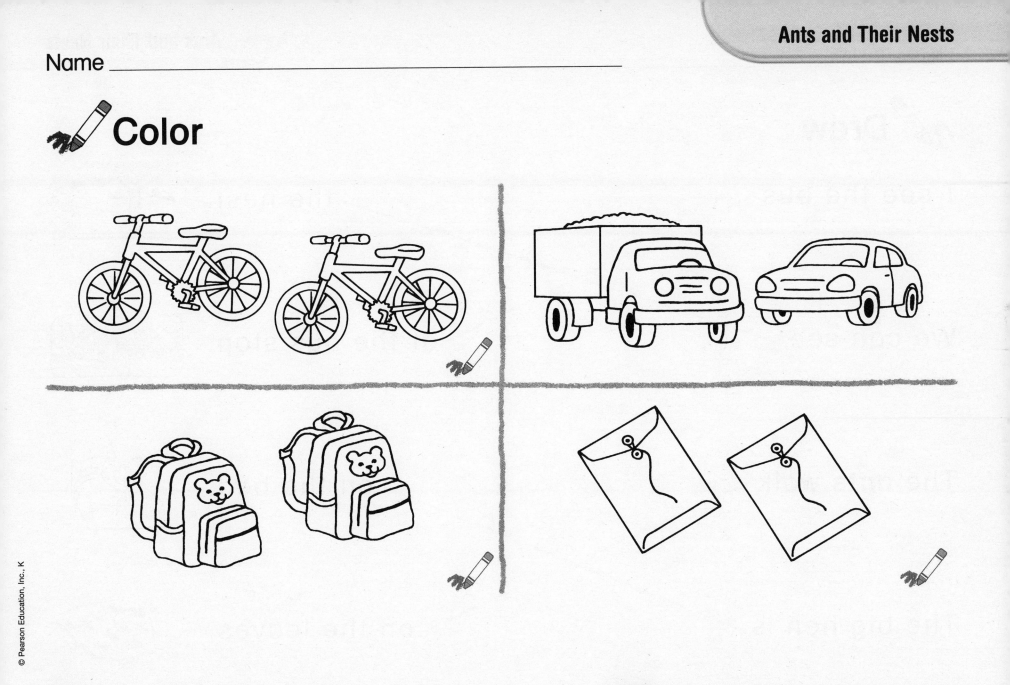

## Color

 **Home Activity:** Have your child tell how the pairs of pictures are alike or different.

**Comprehension** Compare and Contrast  **475**

© Pearson Education, Inc., K

Name _____

# ✏️ Draw

I see the bus

We can see

the nest.

at the bus stop.

The ants walk

The big hen is

on the bed.

on the leaves.

© Pearson Education, Inc., K

**Directions** Read the sentence parts. Draw lines to make complete sentences and read them.

**School + Home** **Home Activity** Begin a sentence and have your child complete the sentence. Then take turns completing each other's sentences.

Name _____

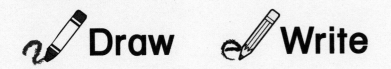 **Draw** **Write**

I will add this to my draft.

_____

- - - - - - - - - - - - - - - - - - - - - - - - - - - - - - - - - - -

_____

_____

- - - - - - - - - - - - - - - - - - - - - - - - - - - - - - - - - - -

**Pictures and answers will vary.**

**Directions** Have children draw pictures of and write or dictate additional information that could be included in the class report.

 **Home Activity** Have your child tell you how the class revised the report to make it better.

Name _____

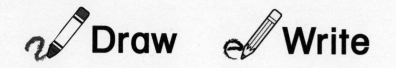 Draw ✏️ Write

**Pictures and answers will vary.**

 **Directions** Have children draw, write, or dictate the entire class report.

 **Home Activity** Discuss with your child another topic he or she would like to write about. Try drafting a report on this topic.

Name _____

✏️ Circle  ✏️ Write

**1.** a bird (is in) the (nest.)

_____

- - - - - - - - - - - - - - - - - - - - - - - - - -

_____

**2.** birds (use grass.)

_____

- - - - - - - - - - - - - - - - - - - - - - - - - -

_____

**3.** we (learned about) birds.

_____

- - - - - - - - - - - - - - - - - - - - - - - - - -

_____

 **Directions** Have children circle the mistakes and rewrite the words or sentences correctly on the lines.

 **Home Activity** Have your child point out and explain his or her edits.

Name _____

✏️ **Circle**   ✏️ **Write**

I shared my selection with __ **Answers will vary.** _____.

Here's what he/she learned.

_____

_____

_____

_____

🍎 **Directions** Have children circle the picture that shows with whom they shared their report. Then have children ask the peer or adult reviewer to fill in the blanks and to discuss the report with him or her.

 **School + Home**   **Home Activity** Ask your child to read or tell the class report to you.